OAKLAND COMMUNITY COLLEGE
HIGHLAND LAKES LIBRARY
7350 COOLEY LAKE ROAD
UNION LAKE MICHIGAN 48085

QK
882
.K3

Kamen, Martin D.

Primary processes in photosynthesis

D1263195

OAKLAND COMMUNITY COLLEGE
HIGHLAND LAKES LIBRARY
7350 COOLEY LAKE ROAD
UNION LAKE MICHIGAN 48085

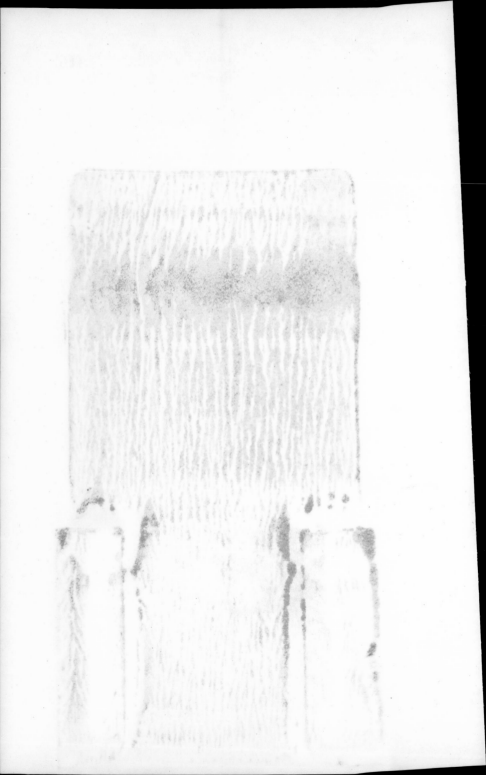

Primary Processes
in
Photosynthesis

ADVANCED BIOCHEMISTRY

A SERIES OF MONOGRAPHS

EDITOR

ANTHONY SAN PIETRO

Charles F. Kettering Research Laboratory
Yellow Springs, Ohio

ooooooooooooooooooooooooooooooooooooooooooooooooooooooooooooooooooooooooooooooooooooooooooooooooooooo

Primary Processes
in
Photosynthesis

MARTIN D. KAMEN

University of California, San Diego
La Jolla, California

1963

ACADEMIC PRESS
New York and London

COPYRIGHT © 1963, BY ACADEMIC PRESS INC.
ALL RIGHTS RESERVED.
NO PART OF THIS BOOK MAY BE REPRODUCED IN ANY FORM,
BY PHOTOSTAT, MICROFILM, OR ANY OTHER MEANS, WITHOUT
WRITTEN PERMISSION FROM THE PUBLISHERS.

ACADEMIC PRESS INC.
111 Fifth Avenue, New York 3, New York

United Kingdom Edition published by
ACADEMIC PRESS INC. (LONDON) LTD.
Berkeley Square House, London W.1

LIBRARY OF CONGRESS CATALOG CARD NUMBER: 63-16965

PRINTED IN THE UNITED STATES OF AMERICA

Sorghum chloroplasts. Top: *Sorghum saccharatum* mesophyll chloroplasts. × 64,000. Lower left: Section from top. × 120,000. Lower right: Section from top. × 800,000. Areas which correspond are outlined and indicated by arrows.

Courtesy, Dr. J. D. McLean, see J. L. Farrant and J. D. McLean, *Proc. European Reg. Conf. Electron Microscopy, Delft, 1960,* **2,** 1039 (1961).

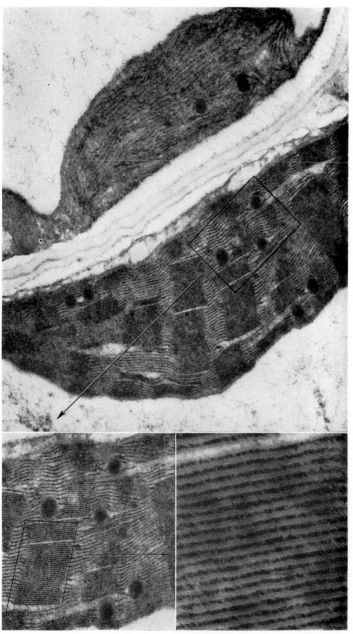

Sorghum chloroplasts

Author's Preface

The shift in emphasis from the study of secondary to the study of primary processes in photosynthesis has generated a need for a text which can serve not only as an introduction for novices but also as an aid to those, expert in the older knowledge, who must accommodate themselves to rapid new developments in fields with the language of which they are not conversant. Such a text must not only present a clear account of present trends and underlying basic concepts, but must also relate these to older knowledge which still retains usefulness and validity. Moreover, it is essential that the resultant book be a small one.

I have approached this task in what I believe to be a wholly novel way, based on the emphasis of comparative aspects and relationships between the various sciences involved. By analysis of the photosynthetic process into successive "eras," the interrelation of the various disciplines is clearly outlined so that the reader, whether a novice or a sophisticate, can obtain a useful perspective of the process as a whole. This, together with a statement of a simple systematics, comprises the first chapter and sets the stage for the discussion of the photosynthetic apparatus in the second chapter, and the presentation of the picture of the primary processes given in the remaining two chapters.

This book ends where others begin. It deals only with events which precede the appearance of the more familiar secondary processes. The thesis is that much of the excitement is over by the time identifiable chemical products of photosynthesis appear. The bridge to the conventional text is supplied in a companion volume on biochemical aspects, written by Dr. A. San Pietro, the Editor of this series. These two volumes together should provide readers at all levels of sophistication with an adequate guide to the rapidly proliferating literature of modern photosynthetic research.

There is one hazard which plagues all writers on photosynthesis and which is best stated in terms of the famous saying, often quoted by C. F. Kettering and attributed to some early American sage: "It's not the things you know that kill you; it's the things you know that ain't so." My hope is that few "ain't so" statements have crept in.

With a few exceptions, no papers later than the end of 1960 were considered in the preparation of this text. This cutoff at 1960 coincides with the onset of a particularly active and fruitful period of photosynthesis research, which is still continuing and shows evidence of an acceleration in the rate of solid achievement. Although obsolescence of some material presented is inevitable, this should not handicap the reader because the emphasis is placed first on principles, rather than whatever factual aspects may be prominent at this particular stage in the development of the field.

As an aid in achieving continuity with the field as it develops, an extensive bibliography has been provided so that the reader will know the laboratories and investigators now active and the likely sources for modification of material in this text.

It is a pleasure to acknowledge the editorial assistance of Mrs. M. C. Bartsch and the suggestions of Beka Doherty Kamen in the preparations of the first draft, as well as the work of Miss S. Hosmer who typed portions of the final draft. I am most particularly indebted to Dr. M. Gonterman and Dr. D. Mauzerall for their careful reading of the text and for suggestions and corrections that they made. Various colleagues extended gracious permission to reproduce figures and illustrations. Acknowledgements are included at appropriate places in the text.

MARTIN D. KAMEN

University of California, San Diego
October, 1963

Editor's Preface

The vistas of biochemical research have been so greatly extended within recent years that it is virtually impossible to remain abreast of all present-day advances. The result has been that most scientists are forced to limit their attention only to that portion of the scientific literature which deals directly with their area of specialization. Of even more serious consequence is the fact that much of the graduate teaching in biochemistry in this country has become extremely specialized in its coverage.

Although the present series was designed primarily for the graduate student in the biological sciences, this does not preclude its usefulness to the research scientist. It is expected that each monograph will provide an introduction to one major area in biochemistry, with particular emphasis on the problems currently under investigation and the experimental procedures employed. The goal of the series is to provide the graduate student with insight and understanding of the scientific approach to problems of a biochemical nature. The extent to which this is achieved will determine the success of the series.

I wish to express my gratitude to all authors of individual monographs and especially to Dr. Martin Kamen for the conscientious preparation of this monograph, which is the first in the series. I am indebted to the staff of Academic Press for their unbounded patience and kindness during the preparation of this work.

ANTHONY SAN PIETRO

Yellow Springs, Ohio
August, 1963

Contents

CHAPTER 1

The Natural History of Photosynthesis

CHAPTER 2

The Photosynthetic Apparatus

CHAPTER 3

The Era of Radiation Physics: pt_s 15 to pt_s 9

CHAPTER 4

The Era of Photochemistry: pt$_s$ 9 to pt$_s$ 4

CHAPTER I

The Natural History of Photosynthesis

I. Definitions

Few phenomena in natural science equal photosynthesis in sweep and grandeur. It suffices to cite as evidence the annual yield of organic matter from photosynthesis which is estimated to be between 10^{10} and 10^{11} tons—an amount equivalent to the weight of a square slab of concrete some hundreds of miles on the side and several stories high, or the weight of metropolitan New York City.

Before anything more is said about photosynthesis, it should be defined. But making a definition of so complex a process is not easy. Photosynthesis begins in the recesses of radiation physics and ends in the far reaches of ecology. Investigators from every branch of science can probe it, and must, if it is to be understood completely.

In the present state of knowledge, any definition tends to be an oversimplification which reveals more about the observer than the process. I may begin with this statement. *Photosynthesis is a series of processes in which electromagnetic energy is converted to chemical free energy which can be used for biosynthesis.*

This rather noncommittal definition, which hardly warrants italics, bears no obvious relation to those usually encountered in textbooks on general biology or chemistry. Most commonly, photosynthesis is thought of as a process in which green plants, with the aid of chlorophyll and light, convert carbon dioxide and water to carbohydrate and molecular oxygen. Variations on this theme occur in which the carbohydrate may be formaldehyde, glucose, or starch. This concept prevails among all sections of the literate pub-

lic. In a few specialized monographs the occurrence of photosynthesis in bacteria and other living systems is recognized,
but only rarely are such phenomena considered as other than
atypical or of secondary importance. In more sophisticated
treatises, the attempt is made to achieve some resolution
of the various processes involved. Often the primary process is described as a "photolysis of water" in which assimilation of carbon dioxide is coupled with secondary nonphotochemical processes.

II. A Small Aside on Traditional Attitudes

The Idols of the Tribe, the Idols of the Cave, the Idols
of the Market Place, the Idols of the Theater—these, the
reader will recall, were the demons Francis Bacon set out
to exorcise over three centuries ago. These idols were his
symbols for intellectual frailties, such as premature generalization, specious rationalization, and semantic confu-
sion.

Among investigators of photosynthesis, as among humans
in general, there are found many addicted to the worship
of these idols. This idolatry is characterized by two massive
syndromes which may be termed "mammalian chauvinism"
and "temporal solipsism."

When mammalian chauvinism holds sway, the victims
ascribe primary importance only to those aspects of photosynthesis which produce results directly beneficial to mam-
mals, and, in particular, to that major aerobe, man. Hence,
their analysis is dominated by awareness of the phenomenon of oxygen production which, in turn, leads to their
neglect of processes in which photosynthesis is not characterized by oxygen evolution.

A leader in the reaction against mammalian chauvinism
has been the distinguished microbiologist, C. B. Van Niel,
whose vigorous espousal of the comparative biochemical
viewpoint (1) has done much to liberate research from its
unbalanced emphasis of green plant photosynthesis.

When temporal solipsism is dominant, its victims accord attention only to events which occur in intervals of time they can sense or measure directly. This condition is probably more widespread than mammalian chauvinism. To overcome this condition, it is necessary to "think exponentially," that is, one must learn to regard the time interval between 10^{-15} and 10^{-14} seconds as of an importance comparable to that between 10^1 and 10^2 seconds. Both involve equal changes in magnitude. As I will attempt to make clear in the next section, the habit of thinking in magnitudes of time will lead to a perception of the photosynthetic process which minimizes effects of such conditions as mammalian chauvinism and temporal solipsism, in which, to quote Bacon, "everyone has a cave or den of his own which defracts and discolours the light of nature."

III. The Time Sequence in Photosynthesis

I propose to start with an analysis of photosynthesis as a sequence of events which occur in successive "eras." Figure 1 shows a scheme for such an analysis. It is convenient to adopt, as an expression of time magnitude, the common logarithm of time in seconds. By analogy with the well-known symbol "p," which stands for "logarithm of reciprocal of" in symbolic expressions such as pH, pK, etc., "pt$_s$" will stand as an abbreviation for "logarithm of the reciprocal of time, expressed in seconds." [1]

Thus, the era between 10^{-15} and 10^{-9} seconds is expressed as pt$_s$ +15 to pt$_s$ +9. This happens to be the time interval which includes the first, or strictly physical, phase of photosynthesis. This era begins with the absorption of the radiant energy as a quantum of visible or infrared light. The limit of pt$_s$ +15, as well as all the others shown between the successive eras, as pictured in Fig. 1, will be rationalized in succeeding chapters. It suffices to state here

[1] I am indebted to Professor D. Gutsche, Washington University, St. Louis, Missouri, for this suggestion.

that the time required for completion of the primary absorption act corresponds to the extreme limit of pt_s +15.

The physical phase continues through the initial con-

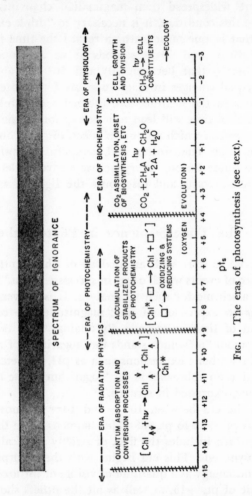

FIG. 1. The eras of photosynthesis (see text).

version of the quantum energy to its first level of stabilization as excitation energy for the primary photochemical process. This stabilization must occur before pt_s 9, as this is the limit set by the possibility that the initial quantum absorption may be reversed by loss of light energy through re-emission as fluorescence. There is possible a dispensation for a longer time period with a limit of pt_s 5, because the excitation energy may be stabilized further by formation of a so-called "metastable triplet" state. However, this possibility is set aside for the present, and pt_s 9 is chosen as the extreme limit on the long time side of the physical era. This gives six orders of magnitude in time for processes involving radiation and solid state physics.

Next, starting at pt_s 9, perhaps sooner, and extending to the time when enzyme-catalyzed chemical reactions inaugurate biochemistry, there is the era of photochemistry. Because enzyme reactions have turnover times with characteristic values no faster than pt_s 4 to 3, the photochemistry phase is set between the limits pt_s 9 and pt_s 4. The photochemistry which occurs in this era completes the conversion of quantum energy to free energy which is available for biochemistry and synthesis. This process lasts five orders of magnitude in time.

With the onset of the biochemical era, there are encountered for the first time processes which effect carbon dioxide assimilation, biosynthesis, and, in the particular case of green plant photosynthesis, evolution of molecular oxygen. Thus, only after passage through eleven orders of magnitude in time, eleven pt_s units, does one arrive at a point where most textbook expositions of photosynthesis begin!

The biochemical era lasts until it merges into the physiological era. The slowest biochemical reactions which correspond to cellular synthesis have turnover times which set the upper limit in time at pt_s -1. Somewhere in the era pt_s $+1$ to pt_s -1, one may discern the beginning of physiology—the interplay of biochemical metabolism and cellular organization. This physiological era may be said to end with the replication of the cell at pt_s -3 to pt_s -4. Beyond this, there is the domain, or era, of botany and ecology.

From the beginning to the end of this process, one notes a total time lapse extending from pt_s $+15$ to pt_s -4, some nineteen orders of magnitude in time expressed in seconds. It is sobering to note that the whole history of the cosmos, in years, is estimated to be only ten or eleven orders of magnitude in time. Thus, the reader can appreciate the vast sweep of photosynthesis, when expressed relative to the pt_s unit, even though such a unit is admittedly an artifice for telescoping events in time.

The problems of interest to contemporary research can be presented also in Fig. 1 by assigning a density of shading to each era shown. The density at each point is proportional to the ignorance about the nature of the process at that point. Greater density of shading implies greater ignorance. The reader will see that, relatively speaking, more is known at the extreme ends of the photosynthetic process and little in the middle. At pt_s 15, there is much factual and theoretical knowledge which belongs in the general area of radiation physics, and which can be applied to achieve some understanding of the act of quantum absorption. Almost immediately, say at pt_s 13, ignorance begins to increase, reflecting the small store of facts about the structure of the photoactive unit functional in the energy conversion process. Still, there is a great reservoir of solid state physics to lighten the gloom in this era.

The shades deepen on approach to pt_s 9, the era of photochemistry, for now there is inadequate theoretical knowledge and there are few facts. The emergence into light does not begin until somewhere in the biochemical era, pt_s 3, and becomes more pronounced, until one stands at pt_s −1 and beyond, in eras descriptions of which include all the vast amount of literature on photosynthesis compiled by botanists, plant physiologists, and farmers.

The passage through all these eras requires learning the languages of radiation physics, solid state physics, photochemistry of condensed systems, quantum chemistry, biochemistry, enzymology, plant physiology, and descriptive biology. It is hardly surprising that lack of communication often exists among different investigators in the many areas of photosynthetic research.

IV. Another Look at Definitions

Now, imagine the sorts of definitions the various eras of photosynthesis might inspire. The temporal solipsist, making a living as a radiation physicist, will see only from pt_s 15 to pt_s 9, or perhaps to pt_s 5—not such a small vista! He may propose to define photosynthesis as "a process in which quanta absorbed in a semi-ordered aggregate are converted and trapped with high efficiency in various metastable states of electronic excitation." If he is pressed to present a formulation of this process, he will write an expression such as that shown in the box for the physical era in Fig. 1, i.e.,

$$\text{Chl}_{\uparrow\downarrow} \xrightarrow{h\nu} \text{Chl}_{\uparrow}^{\downarrow} \text{ and/or } \text{Chl}_{\uparrow}^{\uparrow} \tag{1}$$

where "Chl" stands for the photoactive compound, that is, chlorophyll, bacteriochlorophyll, bacterioviridin, etc. The meaning of this equation, with its various symbols, will be elaborated in Chapter III.

The temporal solipsist, whose profession is that of photochemist, will see little but the era from pt_s 9 to pt_s 4. This, again, is no small reach in time. His definition might be that photosynthesis is a process "in which electronic excitation states of chlorophyll (bacteriochlorophyll, etc.) are selectively quenched in a series of chemical reactions leading to production of stabilized (ground-state) energy-rich systems characterized both by electron excess and by electron deficiency." A formulation based on the era of photochemistry could look like the symbolic reaction shown in Fig. 1, i.e.,

$$\text{Chl}^* \cdot \square \to \text{Chl} + \square' \quad \begin{array}{c} \nearrow \text{oxidants} \\ \searrow \text{reductants} \end{array} \tag{2}$$

An explanation of the meaning of these symbols must be deferred to Chapter IV.

The biochemist, whose temporal solipsism constrains his

attention to pt_s +4 to pt_s −1, will see the reactions involved in carbon dioxide assimilation, oxygen evolution, and metabolism of organic substrates. He will be many eras removed from the quantum process. Most of what he sees will be the nonphotochemical phases of photosynthesis. His definition of photosynthesis will convey the notion of a process in which a photochemical act causes "dehydrogenation of hydrogen donors and reduction of carbon dioxide, mediated by simultaneous synthesis of 'energy-rich' catalysts, such as adenosine triphosphate, acylated coenzymes, etc." A simple formulation will be the reaction, originally proposed by Van Niel, shown in Fig. 1, i.e.,

$$CO_2 + 2H_2A \xrightarrow{h\nu} CH_2O + 2A + H_2O \qquad (3)$$

where "H_2A" is a general hydrogen donor, "A" is a radical (organic or inorganic) generated by oxidation of H_2A, and "CH_2O" is cellular material in which carbon is at the oxidation level of carbohydrate.

The plant physiologist, constrained to pt_s 1 and beyond, will think of photosynthesis as a process in which "cellular growth is supported at the expense of light energy absorbed by chlorophyll." He will be addicted to proposals such as the classic equation,

$$6CO_2 + 6H_2O \xrightarrow{h\nu} 6O_2 + C_6H_{12}O_6 \qquad (4)$$

or perhaps its less committal generalization,

$$nCO_2 + nH_2O \xrightarrow{h\nu} nO_2 + (CH_2O)_n \qquad (5)$$

The bacterial physiologist, seeing as products no oxygen and often little carbohydrate, will be no less a temporal solipsist and will revert to some form of Eq. (3).

The reader, by now, will feel that I have labored this matter of definition sufficiently. He will also feel that a general definition, satisfactory to all concerned, must remain no more specific than some general statement such as that proposed at the beginning of this chapter.

V. Systematics of Photosynthesis

The various photosyntheses are classified traditionally on the basis of nutritional requirements for growth. Usually, the *minimal requirement for photosynthetic growth* is chosen as a decisive criterion. This means that the point of reference is taken somewhere at the end of the natural history of the process, i.e., at $pt_s \sim -3$). Only a limited systematics can result from the use of such a reference point.

A more fundamental system of classification requires that a point of reference be picked as near to the onset of chemistry as is possible, to permit a generally valid statement in terms of the simplest possible stoichiometry. In the present state of knowledge, as one may infer from the spectrum of ignorance in Fig. 1, such a point will be somewhere at the start of the biochemical era ($pt_s \sim +3$). Future progress will see the point of reference pushed further toward the left in Fig. 1.

Before attempting to set up a system for classifying the various photosyntheses, it will be convenient to use the concept of a chemical process as a sum of partial reversible processes, and, in particular, of processes which can be expressed as partial reversible "electrode" reactions. These can be imagined to occur at the electrodes of a galvanic cell set up so that the summation of the electrode reactions, as written, yields the over-all process in question, as well as the free energy change involved. In applying such a procedure to photosynthesis, one must identify reactants and products in some stoichiometric relations and in defined standard states. Further, one must find a reaction in terms of which all others that are known can be included, at least insofar as total energy requirements are concerned.

Photosynthesis, as performed by green plants, has a special advantage with respect to energy requirement, because it alone exhibits two simultaneous energy-storing processes, which are apparently independent. One of these is the reduction of carbon from its "reduction level" in CO_2 to an average reduction level close to that in cellular carbon.[2] The other is the production of oxygen essentially from water. The carbon reduction process requires a free energy change which approximates 25–30 kcal/mole of CO_2 assimilated. The oxygen evolution requires considerably more energy, of the order ~80–100 kcal/mole.

These energy requirements can be understood qualitatively by noting the energies of combustion of the single bonds involved. In the system "CO_2/CH_2O," one replaces two C—O bonds (~70 kcal/mole) by two C—H bonds (~87 kcal/mole). Thus, one finds an energy debt of approximately $2 \times 17 = 34$ kcal/atom/mole. In the system "H_2O/O_2," two O—H bonds (~110 kcal/mole) are replaced by two O—O bonds (~35 kcal/mole), so that ~75 kcal are needed per atom O.

The process of green plant photosynthesis presents the largest energy requirement that is known among all photosyntheses. Hence, a general system based on the stoichiometry of the green plant process is most comprehensive, at least as far as energetics are concerned.

First, it is reasonable to assume that one electrode reaction should be picked to describe a system at an oxidation potential close to that for the ideal (reversible) oxygen electrode; the reaction, per electron, is

$$\tfrac{1}{4}O_2 + H^+ + \epsilon^- \rightarrow \tfrac{1}{2}H_2O \qquad (6)$$

The standard oxidation potential of Eq. (6) is $+1.23$ volts

[2] To quantitate these statements in terms of "reduction level" in the sense commonly employed [E. I. Rabinowitch, "Photosynthesis," 2nd ed., Wiley (Interscience), New York (1951)], define the reduction level as the ratio of the total number of oxygen molecules needed for complete combustion to the number of oxygen molecules needed for combustion of the carbon atoms present. As an example, for a carbon compound which contains n_C atoms of carbon, n_H atoms of hydrogen, and n_O atoms of oxygen, the reduction level would be $[2n_C + 0.5n_H - n_O]$ / $2n_C$. If the compound is a carbohydrate, i.e., $n_O = 0.5n_H$, then the reduction level is one. The most reduced carbon (CH_4) has a reduction level of two, the most oxidized (CO_2) a reduction level of zero.

relative to that of the standard hydrogen electrode. It is immaterial for present purposes that no one has ever seen a reversible oxygen electrode, or that the mechanism for extraction of electrons from water is unknown. One is interested only in a theoretical electrode reaction which involves a definite potential as one part of an electrochemical system, equivalent to a process in which oxygen is liberated from water.

The other electrode reaction depends on the assumption that all photosyntheses can use CO_2 as a single carbon source. This means one needs an electrode reaction with potential sufficient to supply electrons spontaneously to CO_2 in a process which raises the reduction level of the carbon to that which it possesses in carbohydrate or cell material of equivalent reduction level. The simplest assumption is to postulate the hydrogen electrode reaction itself, with its standard potential of zero volts; at physiological pH ($\sim$7) the potential of the hydrogen electrode is ~ -0.4 volts, a value sufficiently negative to drive electrons on to CO_2 in any process in which CO_2 is likely to act as an electron acceptor in cell synthesis. Thus, the second electrode reaction is

$$\epsilon^- + H^+ \rightarrow \frac{1}{2}H_2 \tag{7}$$

The effective potential to use (-0.4 volts) is that for hydrogen at atmospheric pressure and (H^+) at an activity of 10^{-7} moles per liter.

For oxygen, the variation in potential determined against the hydrogen electrode (E_h) is given (2) by the relation

$$E_h = 1.23 + 0.0148 \log P_{O_2} - 0.06 \text{ pH} \tag{8}$$

At pH 7 and where $P_{O_2} = 1$ atmosphere, E_h for the oxygen electrode is $\sim +0.81$ volts.

These values for the hydrogen and oxygen electrodes can be used to express the conditions that must prevail if there is to be simultaneous reduction of CO_2 and production of O_2 in the stoichiometric relation which has been determined to hold in steady-state photosynthesis by green plants. This, in its simplest form, is

$$CO_2 + H_2O \rightarrow CH_2O + O_2 \tag{9}$$

In Fig. 2, there is displayed an electrochemical oxidation potential diagram of a type employed commonly, except that the hydrogen electrode reaction is placed at the top ($E_h \sim -0.4$ volts) and the oxygen electrode reaction at the

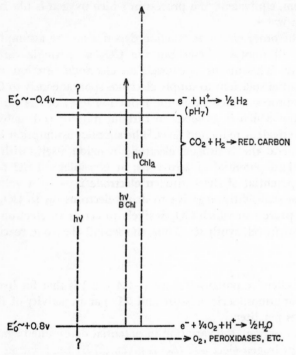

FIG. 2. Electrochemical equivalence scale for over-all photosynthetic energy storage process (see text).

bottom ($E_h \sim +0.8$ volts). The convention of signs and system of writing reactions is that favored by biochemists. Thus, the oxygen electrode reaction, as written, has a positive potential. Hence its free energy change (ΔG) is negative and equal to -0.8 electron-volts of maximum reversible work. Because ΔG is negative, the reaction as written is spontaneous, a fact which is consistent with the known chemistry of oxygen. The hydrogen electrode reaction, with its negative E_h and positive ΔG, is not spontaneous as written. It proceeds spontaneously in the reverse direction because the activity of the (H$^+$) at neutral pH is less than that of (H$^+$) in its standard state.

If one subtracts the oxygen reaction from the hydrogen reaction as written, there results the over-all reaction

$$\tfrac{1}{2}H_2O \rightarrow \tfrac{1}{2}H_2 + \tfrac{1}{4}O_2 \tag{10}$$

with all reactants and products in standard states. The ΔE_h is -1.2 volts; the corresponding ΔG is $+1.2$ volt-equivalents. Because ΔG is positive, this reaction, as written, proceeds spontaneously from right to left. Alternatively, for each oxidation equivalent, 1.2 volt-equivalents of free energy are needed to drive the reaction from left to right. To produce a molecule of oxygen, four oxidizing equivalents are needed, or $4 \times 1.2 = 4.8$ volt-equivalents of free energy. Since 1 volt-equivalent is $\sim$23,000 cal/mole-equivalent, one deduces that $4.8 \times 23,000$ cal or 112 kcal are needed per mole of O_2 produced or CO_2 reduced. Thus, this procedure of analysis with two electrode reactions [Eqs. (6) and (7)] gives results which are consistent with the known thermochemistry of the process symbolized by Eq. (10).

This way of thinking about the energy requirement of photosynthesis seems convenient and simple. It emphasizes the essential process which is the removal of electrons from a region of "low" potential (high electron affinity) to one of "high" potential (low electron affinity); that is, it visualizes photosynthesis as a process in which the binding energy of the electron is changed from the value it has in the environment supplied by the water-CO_2 system to that encountered in the carbohydrate-oxygen system. In terms of Fig. 2, electrons are "pumped up" from oxygen to hydrogen. This requires pushing the electrons against a potential gradient of 1.2 volts.

The work done is accomplished at the expense of light energy contained in the absorbed packets of electromagnetic energy, known as "quanta." Each quantum absorbed must supply sufficient energy, after transformation and conversion to electronic excitation energy, to equal at least 1.2 volt-electrons of energy. The energy content (E) of a photon (quantum of electromagnetic radiation) is given by the well-known relation postulated in wave mechanics, i.e.,

$$E = hc/\lambda \tag{11}$$

where h is Planck's constant (6.6×10^{-27} erg-sec), c is the velocity of the electromagnetic radiation wave packet (equal to the velocity of light) which is 3×10^{10} cm/sec, and λ is the wavelength in centimeters. Substitution of these values, with conversion of E in ergs to volt-electrons (ev) and λ to angstrom units, gives the relation[3]

$$E_{ev} = 12,350/\lambda_{\text{Å}} \tag{12}$$

Thus, each quantum effective in green plant photosynthesis ($\lambda \sim 6800$ Å) has a "potency," or energy equivalent, of ~ 1.8 ev. In Fig. 2, this is shown by the dotted arrow, labeled "$h\nu_{\text{Chl}_a}$," for the characteristic quantum absorbed in the red band of chlorophyll a (see Chapter 3). In certain bacterial photosyntheses, the absorption band of the active pigment, bacteriochlorophyll, with lowest energy is in the infrared ($\lambda \sim 9000$ Å), and so the potency of the quantum absorbed is ~ 1.3 ev, shown as "$h\nu_{\text{BChl}}$."

Hence, any of the quanta which are effective in photosynthesis have sufficient potency to drive electrons against a potential gradient of 1.2 volts. Now, one may ask where the starting points and the termini of the electrons are located on the potential ladder of Fig. 2.

Obviously, with no more information, one may arbitrarily select any range of potential values. If it is assumed that in *all* photosyntheses—plant or bacterial—the initial products are identical and in equilibrium with the oxygen of water, then one of the two potentials can be chosen as that of the oxygen electrode. Assuming further that all electrons are

$$[3]\; E_{ev} = \frac{(6.6 \times 10^{-27} \text{ erg-sec})\left(\dfrac{1}{1.6 \times 10^{-12}} \text{ ev/erg}\right)(3 \times 10^{10} \text{ cm/sec})}{(10^{-8} \text{ cm/Å})}$$

pushed to the potential level of the hydrogen electrode, and that the initial products are also in equilibrium with the hydrogen of water, there results the postulate of "water photolysis."

The reader is now in a position to comprehend such a statement as this: "The primary reaction in photosynthesis is the photolysis of water, represented by the reaction $HOH \rightarrow [H] + [OH]$, where the brackets do not indicate production of H and OH radicals as such, but of two systems formally equivalent to such products." This representation of photosynthesis, so often heard in discussions of the subject, causes much difficulty for novices who find it hard to understand what is meant by specifying reaction products which are "something formally equivalent to," but really "something else." The statement is of the "as if" variety; thus, "the result of all photochemical phases of photosynthesis is *as if* electrons had migrated against a potential gradient equivalent to that required energetically to effect a fission of water into hydrogen and oxygen." Any process which involves an amount of electrical work equivalent to that shown for the process of Fig. 2 is equivalent, in terms of energy requirement, to a photolysis of water. It is "formally" equivalent if the products are in equilibrium, however remote, with the oxygen and hydrogen of water.

What is the justification for this arbitrary assignment of potentials in Fig. 2? Only that it provides a simple bookkeeping device for constructing a systematic classification of photosynthesis. The following considerations will show how it works in general, and in some special cases.

One may write for the general case [Eq. (13) below], as Van Niel first proposed [*vide* Eq. (3)], the scheme represented by Eqs. (a), (b), and (c).

$$
\begin{array}{ll}
4HOH \rightarrow 4H + 4OH & \text{(a)} \\
4H + CO_2 \rightarrow CH_2O + H_2O & \text{(b)} \\
\underline{4OH + 2H_2A \rightarrow 2A + 4H_2O} & \text{(c)} \\
CO_2 + 2H_2A \rightarrow CH_2O + 2A + H_2O & [\Sigma(a + b + c)] \quad (13)
\end{array}
$$

Here one sees that movement of four oxidizing equivalents with concomitant production of four reducing equivalents

(a) begins the process pictured in Fig. 2. The use of the symbols "H" and "OH" for these two product systems recognizes the assumption of equilibration with water, hydrogen, and oxygen for purposes of stoichiometry, but *not* mechanism.

The following processes, (b) and (c), clearly state that the character of the carbon metabolism depends both on the assimilation of CO_2 and on the nature of the general hydrogen donor, H_2A. In addition, the character of the oxidized product, A, is determined by H_2A.

Now consider the bacterial photosynthesis with CO_2 in the presence of H_2S [Eqs. (a), (b), (c), and (14)].

$$
\begin{array}{lll}
4HOH & \rightarrow 4H + 4OH & \text{(a)} \\
4OH + 2H_2S & \rightarrow 2S + 4H_2O & \text{(b)} \\
\underline{4H + CO_2 \quad \rightarrow CH_2O + H_2O} & & \text{(c)} \\
CO_2 + 2H_2S \rightarrow CH_2O + 2S + H_2O & [\Sigma(a+b+c)] & \text{(14)}
\end{array}
$$

Equation (14) is closely analogous to that of green plant photosynthesis, from which it can be derived merely by replacement of H_2O with H_2S. Thus the traditional case of green plant photosynthesis is described by (15).

$$
\begin{array}{lll}
4HOH & \rightarrow 4H + 4OH & \text{(a)} \\
4OH & \rightarrow O_2 + 2H_2O & \text{(b)} \\
\underline{4H + CO_2 \quad \rightarrow CH_2O + H_2O} & & \text{(c)} \\
CO_2 + H_2O \rightarrow CH_2O + O_2 & [\Sigma(a+b+c)] & \text{(15)}
\end{array}
$$

When H_2A falls in the class of organic hydrogen donors, the equations lose their ready resemblance to (15), because CO_2 is no longer the sole carbon source; the organic radicals formed by dehydrogenation of H_2A may also be a source of carbon. Application of the general bookkeeping scheme to photometabolism of organic carbon and hydrogen donors is readily accomplished by the following procedure:

1. Calculate the total oxidation equivalents needed to oxidize all carbon atoms to CO_2. Each carbon atom will require four such equivalents.

2. Add the total oxidation equivalents needed for combustion of hydrogen present, one for each hydrogen atom.

3. Subtract the oxidation equivalents present as oxygen, two for each oxygen atom.

4. Begin the assimilation scheme by splitting as many molecules of water as are needed to give the total oxidizing equivalents determined from steps *(1)*, *(2)*, and *(3)*. One molecule of water will yield one oxidation equivalent (represented as "OH") and one reducing equivalent ("H").

5. Assume various integral values for total carbon from the CO_2, generated by oxidation with "OH," which must be reduced with "H" to carbohydrate. Each CO_2 will require four "H" to give one CH_2O and one H_2O.

As an illustration, consider the case of malic acid, a typical organic substrate for photometabolism by certain photosynthetic bacteria. The empirical formula is $C_4H_6O_5$. The total "OH" needed will be $(4 \times 4) + (6 \times 1) - (5 \times 2)$, or twelve. Hence, the first equation (a) for a sequence of reactions (16) will be

$$12HOH \rightarrow 12H + 12OH \qquad (16a)$$

Now use all twelve "OH" to oxidize $C_4H_6O_5$, thus:

$$12OH + C_4H_6O_5 \rightarrow 4CO_2 + 9H_2O \qquad (16b)$$

Next, one may assume that either one, two, or three CH_2O are formed. Then one needs four, eight, or twelve "H," respectively [Eqs. (16c'), (16c''), (16c''')]

$$4H + CO_2 \rightarrow CH_2O + H_2O \qquad (16c')$$
$$8H + 2CO_2 \rightarrow 2CH_2O + 2H_2O \qquad (16c'')$$
$$12H + 3CO_2 \rightarrow 3CH_2O + 3H_2O \qquad (16c''')$$

In the first two cases [(c') and (c'')], there will be excess "H," namely eight "H" and four "H," respectively. In the third case (c'''), both "H" and "OH" are used up completely, and the water contribution is equal on both sides of the over-all equation, which is obtained by addition of the partial reactions. If one assumes that all excess "H" can be eliminated as molecular hydrogen, the following possibilities result for the over-all metabolic fate of malic acid.

$$2H_2O + C_4H_6O_5 \rightarrow CH_2O + 3CO_2 + 4H_2 \qquad [\Sigma(a + b + c')] \qquad (16)$$
$$H_2O + C_4H_6O_5 \rightarrow 2CH_2O + 2CO_2 + 2H_2 \qquad [\Sigma(a + b + c'')] \qquad (16)$$
$$C_4H_6O_5 \rightarrow 3CH_2O + CO_2 \qquad [\Sigma(a + b + c''')] \qquad (16)$$

Of course, it is possible to assume no assimilation, in which

case there is no "photosynthesis"—the result is that all "H"
is eliminated as H_2 and the over-all reaction is:

$$3H_2O + C_4H_6O_5 \rightarrow 4CO_2 + 6H_2 \qquad (16')$$

Excess hydrogen can be disposed of in other ways as well.
Different assumptions about the reduction level of carbon
can also be made.

It is apparent that this procedure, while perhaps enter-
taining, sheds no light on the actual course of photometabolism. However, it affords a ready means for monitor-
ing the complex carbon, hydrogen, and oxygen balance in
photometabolic assimilations of organic material. In actual
practice, (3) the results obtained for photoassimilation of
malate by a typical photosynthetic bacterium, *Rhodospirillum rubrum,* are described formally by Eqs. (16) Σ (a + b +
c") and (16) Σ (a + b + c''').

With this kind of bookkeeping based on a hypothetical
photofission of water, one can describe the systematics for
photosynthesis which are presented by most authorities.
Photosyntheses which proceed as represented formally by
Eq. (15) are confined to green plants, including lower forms,
such as algae and certain protozoa, and higher forms, such
as the leaf-bearing systems. This type of photosynthesis is
the best-known and traditional variety, generally termed
"green plant photosynthesis."

Photosyntheses which proceed as represented formally by
Eq. (14) occur among the green sulfur bacteria (Chloraceae)
and purple sulfur bacteria (Thiorhodaceae). These microorganisms are strict anaerobes and are unable to utilize
sources of energy other than radiation absorbed by their
own pigment systems, particularly near-infrared in the case
of the Thiorhodaceae. The Chloraceae can use only CO_2
as a carbon source and only inorganic hydrogen donors.
Hence, one may classify them as *obligate photoautotrophic
anaerobes.* The Thiorhodaceae can function in the same
way, but in addition they can utilize organic hydrogen
donors. Thus they can be classified both as *photoautotrophic*
and *photoheterotrophic obligate anaerobes.*

Photosyntheses which proceed as formally represented in Eq. (16), and according to the general Eq. (13) with H_2A as an organic hydrogen donor, are found in the nonsulfur purple bacteria (Athiorhodaceae). These bacteria are *obligate heterotrophes,* although they can, in some cases, utilize molecular hydrogen as hydrogen donor and CO_2 as sole carbon source. They require trace amounts of complex organic compounds (vitamins) for growth. In addition, they possess a respiratory metabolism, which can support aerobic growth in the dark, just as in nonphotosynthetic systems such as yeast and *Escherichia coli.* The Athiorhodaceae may be classified as *facultative photoheterotrophes,* with the reservation that their facultative character is rather unusual. Thus, aerobic growth occurs only with respiratory uptake of oxygen in the dark, and anaerobic growth occurs only by photoassimilation of organic material and CO_2 and not, as might be expected, also by fermentation of organic substrates.

In the next chapter other characteristics which distinguish these various photosyntheses will be discussed. For the present, the reader should note what is *common* to all of them from a metabolic standpoint—that *all photosyntheses appear to involve an anaerobic oxidative metabolism which can be linked to a reductive assimilation of CO_2.* The presence of oxygen is incidental only to green plant photosynthesis where it appears as a waste product. Indeed, it is hard to conceive of a process which is more anaerobic than one which not only fails to utilize oxygen but actually eliminates it as a waste product!! Hence, one can conceive of photosynthesis as an assimilatory process in which an anaerobic oxidation-reduction is coupled to photoactivation.

VI. Collateral Reading

In this chapter I have attempted to place before the reader a conceptual background with little depth in detail. Succeeding chapters will deal specifically with the special problems which arise in the photophysical and photochemical eras. The reader is urged to refer to a number of texts which can form the basis for an extended bibliography.

There are three source books of recent publication. The first of these, which is referred to as "I" throughout this book, is the massive set of three volumes by E. I. Rabinowitch, "Photosynthesis" 2nd edition, Vol. 1 and Vol. 2 (2 parts), Wiley (Interscience) New York (1945, 1951, 1956). This monograph deals with every aspect of photosynthesis. Despite its encyclopedic character, the author has endeavored to pick and choose data which are reliable and has, where possible, made critical evaluations of experimental results. The second monograph, which I shall call "II" in subsequent references, is a part of the series "Handbuch der Pflanzenphysiologie," published by Springer-Verlag (Berlin). Volume 5 of this series, edited by W. Ruhland (1960) and entitled "Die CO_2-Assimilation," is in two parts, and contains authoritative articles on the most important aspects of photosynthesis, written by experts in each field of research involved. A third and similar monograph, referred to as "III" in the following chapters, is found in Volume 3 of the treatise "Radiation Biology," edited by A. Hollaender and published by McGraw-Hill Book Co., Inc., New York (1956). The first eleven chapters covering a wide range of topics in photosynthesis are presented by certain of the most highly qualified experts.

In addition, there are a number of symposium volumes, some of more recent vintage, which should be consulted for the presentation of divergent viewpoints maintained at present in the various areas of photosynthetic research as well as for new experimental developments. These are arranged in chronological order and numbered for reference as follows:

1. "Carbon Dioxide Fixation and Photosynthesis," Symposia Soc. Exptl. Biol. No. 5, Academic Press, New York (1951).
2. "Symposium on Autotrophic Microorganisms," Soc. Gen. Microbiol., Cambridge Univ. Press, London and New York (1957).

3. "Research in Photosynthesis," Wiley (Interscience), New York (1957).
4. "The Photochemical Apparatus. Its Structure and Function," Brookhaven Symposium in Biol., No. 11 (1959).
5. "Comparative Biochemistry of Photoreactive Systems," Symposia Comp. Biol., No. 1, Academic Press, New York (1960).
6. "Bioenergetics," Symposium sponsored by U.S. Atomic Energy Commission, Radiation Research, Suppl. 2, Academic Press, New York (1960).
7. Symposium on "Light and Life," McCollum-Pratt Institute, Johns Hopkins Press, Baltimore, Maryland (1961).

Of course, no list is complete without mention of a most useful and excellent little volume by R. Hill and C. P. Whittingham, "Photosynthesis," published in the Methuen monograph series, Methuen, Ltd., London (1955). Finally, there is a scholarly and exhaustive treatment of certain aspects of photosynthesis in an article by H. Gaffron, in Volume IB of the text, "Plant Physiology," Academic Press, New York (1960).

References

1. C. B. Van Niel, *Advances in Enzymol.*, **1**, 263 (1941).
2. W. M. Clark, "Oxidation-Reduction Potentials of Organic Systems," p. 79. Williams & Wilkins, Baltimore, Maryland, 1960.
3. H. Gest, M. D. Kamen, and H. M. Bregoff, *J. Biol. Chem.* **182**, 153 (1950).

CHAPTER II

The Photosynthetic Apparatus

I. Nature and Distribution

Biosynthesis in living cells requires the intervention of highly organized subcellular particulate systems. Representative of such aggregates are the mitochondria and microsomes in nonphotosynthetic organisms. Photochemical biosynthesis is no exception. The entities which are essential in the coupling of photoactivation to biosynthesis are known variously as "chloroplasts," "grana," or "chromatophores," depending on the tissue involved. As may be inferred from these terms,[1] these photoactive subcellular particles are pigmented. In fact, they contain all the photosynthetically active pigments.

The great variation encountered in photosynthetic systems, which range from anaerobic bacteria to the aerobic higher green plants, extends to their photoactive subcellular particles. Isolated chromatophores are spherical or semi-spherical bodies which can be obtained by rupture of photosynthetic bacteria. They may appear as aggregates with major dimensions as great as several hundred millimicrons. Fragmented chromatophores, which retain photosynthetic activity, can be prepared with linear dimensions as small as 20–40 mμ. Chloroplasts, as observed *in vivo* in the higher plants and in some protozoa, are relatively enormous bodies with major dimensions, e.g., of 5–10 μ. They are generally ellipsoidal, disklike bodies which exhibit a variety of internal structures, easily visualized with the electron microscope. Usually they contain lamellar bodies which may be stacked to form thin disks, often referred to as "grana." This

---

[1] Derived from the Greek bases "khloros" (green), "plassein" (to form), "khroma" (color), "pherein" (to bear).

latter term is commonly applied to any one of a complex of variegated structures, intermediate in size between chromatophores and chloroplasts, which are the sites of photosynthetic activity in unicellular blue-green, green, and red algae and which may exhibit many shapes (stars, bands, hemispheres, etc.).

Researches on the morphology of these photoactive particles are of crucial importance because the mechanisms which may be operative in the physical and photochemical eras are determined by details of structure, particularly in the placement and orientation of the quantum-absorbing centers relative to chemical reaction sites. One can expect that all photosynthetic systems will share many structural features. However, it is not likely, in view of the diverse metabolic patterns found in photosynthetic systems, that structural details determined for a particle derived from a given organism will be duplicated precisely in a particle derived from another.

The structures which are presented in nature are not necessarily *minimal* systems for the processes of energy absorption and efficient transformation to biochemically useful free energy. It is obvious, in comparing a bacterial chromatophore or an algal granum with a green plant chloroplast, that many details of structure present in the latter may be of secondary importance for the primary processes involved in the physical and photochemical eras. One may pose these two questions: (*a*) *What is the total molecular composition of the simplest photoactive structure capable of photosynthetic activity?* (*b*) *What is the minimal degree of organization of such a structural entity?*

Although enormous amounts of effort have been expended in research on the morphology and development of the photoactive bodies, particularly of chloroplasts which are most amenable to visualization techniques, there are not definitive answers, as yet, to these questions (1). In this chapter some of the knowledge which has been accumulated concerning the structure of the photosynthetic apparatus will be presented.

II. Chloroplast Composition

A. General Considerations

Any photochemical system can be expected to contain components ("photosensitizers") which initiate reactions by absorption and transformation of radiant energy to produce activated intermediates and nonphotoactive components, which in turn react to carry forward secondary processes and complete the reaction sequence. In the chloroplast, the photosensitizing system consists of tetrapyrrolic chelates of magnesium—*chlorophylls*[2]—and two other major groups of pigments—the fat-soluble *carotenoids* and the water-soluble *phycobilins* or *biliproteins*. The physical and chemical properties of these photoactive components *in vivo* must be inferred more or less indirectly from studies on these components as isolated and purified *in vitro*. In what follows it will be seen that there may be appreciable, and even crucial, differences between *in vivo* and *in vitro* manifestations of a given pigment. Moreover, important components may not be extractable and so must be studied wholly by indirect means (see p. 37 *et seq.*). Finally, it is no simple matter to prepare "pure" chloroplasts or grana, i.e., photoactive cell-free extracts, freed of all other cellular bodies such as mitochondria and cell wall fragments. Indeed, much debate centers about what is meant by "whole" chloroplasts. This difficulty affects particularly determination of the enzyme content of chloroplasts and grana. Recently, R. M. Leech and R. J. Ellis (2) have proposed an enzymatic criterion for purity of chloroplast preparations, based on the claim that glutamic-oxalacetic transaminase is a mitochondrial enzyme and is absent from chloroplasts.[3]

Another aspect of the question about chloroplast integrity is the inability of different laboratories to agree on a procedure for achieving standardization of chloroplast prepara-

[2] Derived from the Greek "khloros" (green) and "phullon" (leaf).

[3] This conclusion requires modification because V. Heber has reported that glutamic-oxalacetic transaminase is present; instead, glutamate-pyruvate transaminase, glutamate dehydrogenase and pyruvate kinase are absent. [See *Z. Naturforsch.* **156,** 100 (1960).]

tions. This is manifest in the literature on the "Hill reaction—the chloroplast-catalyzed photoliberation of oxygen from water in the presence of suitable hydrogen acceptors—wherein many conflicting reports occur about the reproducibility of yields obtainable (3). T. Punnett (4) has suggested a rationale for reconciliation of results from various laboratories based on his finding that most preparations reported have actually been heterogeneous, inadequately stabilized mixtures of particles in varying states of disaggregation.

B. *The Photoactive Pigments*

The earth, viewed from the stratosphere, shows large green areas which owe their color to the fact that the dominant pigment of chloroplasts is chlorophyll *a*. The structure of the monomeric *in vitro* form, to which the term chlorophyll *a* is applied, has been firmly established by total synthesis recently (5). At least three other forms of chlorophyll can be isolated from various sources. These are called chlorophylls *b, c,* and *d*. The structures of these chlorophylls, where known, are shown in Fig. 3A.

Chlorophyll *a* is universally present in the grana or chloroplasts of photosynthetic organisms, e.g., higher green plants, algae, certain protozoa. Chlorophyll *b* occurs largely in higher green plants and green algae. Chlorophyll *c* is found in brown algae, diatoms, and dinoflagellates. Little is known about its structure other than that it is certainly a tetrapyrrolic chelate of magnesium. Chlorophyll *d* occurs in red algae. The most recent studies appear to establish its structure as 2-desvinyl-2-formylchlorophyll *a* (6, 7). Small amounts of a chlorophyll precursor called "protochlorophyll" are present in green plants (8) and algae (9). Protochlorophyll appears to differ from chlorophyll only in that it lacks the two hydrogen atoms at carbons 7 and 8, so that it is the porphyrin analog of chlorophyll. It is found in low concentrations in dark-grown photosynthetic organisms, and is the precursor of chlorophyll in the "greening" reaction (10).

In addition to these chlorophylls, it is useful to know

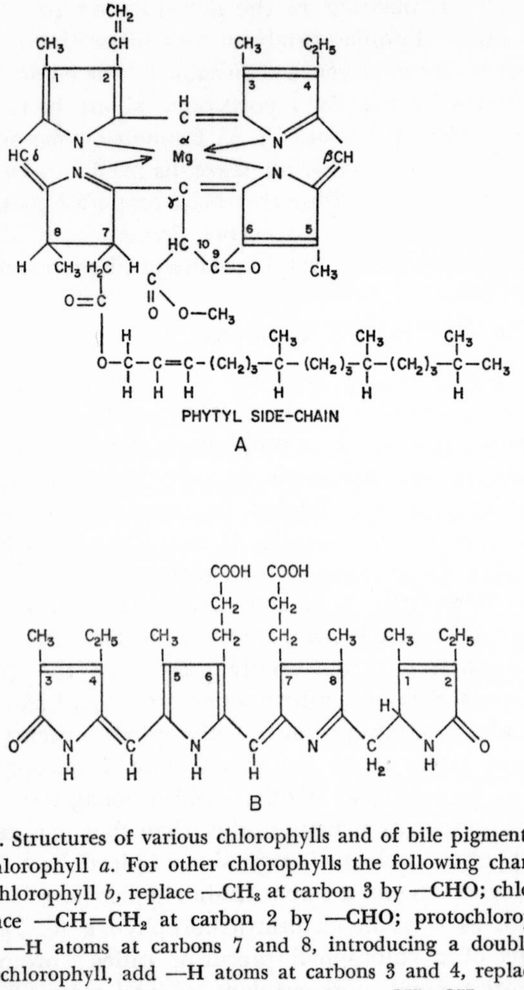

FIG. 3. Structures of various chlorophylls and of bile pigments.

A. Chlorophyll *a*. For other chlorophylls the following changes are made: chlorophyll *b*, replace —CH_3 at carbon 3 by —CHO; chlorophyll *d*, replace —$CH=CH_2$ at carbon 2 by —CHO; protochlorophyll *a*, remove —H atoms at carbons 7 and 8, introducing a double bond; bacteriochlorophyll, add —H atoms at carbons 3 and 4, replacing the double bond with a single bond, and replace —$CH=CH_2$ at carbon 2 by —C—CH_3; *Chlorobium* chlorophyll 660, replace —$CH=CH_2$ at

$$\overset{\|}{O}$$

carbon 2 by —C_2H_5, replace isopentanol ring (carbons 9 and 10) by normal propyl side chain (—C_3H_7).

B. Mesobilivioline (bis-lactam form): prosthetic group of phycocyanin. Mesobilirhodin, the chromaphore thought to be associated with phycoerythrin, is an isomer with one less conjugated double bond.

the following derivatives which are degradation products, formed either during extraction of pigments from living material or by chemical manipulation in quantitative assays. *Pheophytins* are chlorophylls from which magnesium has been removed. *Phyllides* are products of chlorophyll degradation which retain magnesium—i.e., the removal of phytol results in a monobasic acid, the esters of which are *chlorophyllides;* hence, chlorophyll *a* is the phytyl ester of the acid, or phytyl chlorophyllide. The lower chlorophyllides are of practical importance because, unlike the chlorophylls, methyl and ethyl chlorophyllides can be obtained as well-defined crystals. *Phorbides* are formed similarly by removal of phytol from pheophytins.

The second major group of compounds always associated with the pigment complex—the *carotenoids*—are practically all derivatives of the same linear C_{40} skeleton, in which eight isoprenoid (C_5) units are combined so that the two methyl groups at the center of the molecule are positioned 1:6 to each other and the other methyl groups are in 1:5 positions, i.e., as in Fig. 4. Carotenoids are usually subdivided into "carotenes"—hydrocarbon carotenoids—and "xanthophylls"—oxygenated carotenoids. A third class is sometimes mentioned, viz., the "carotenoid acids," in which terminal structures contain acidic carboxylic groups. In green plants the major pigment is β-carotene; α-carotene is often present, too. Five xanthophylls are common constituents. Two of these are oxygenated forms of β-carotene, viz., the 3-hydroxy derivative ("cryptoxanthin") and the 3,3'-dihydroxy derivative ("zeaxanthin"). Another is the 3,3'-dihydroxy derivative of α-carotene ("lutein"). The last two are "violaxanthin" (5,6,5',6'-diepoxyzeaxanthin) and "neoxanthin," the structure of which is unknown. Other oxycarotenoids in small amounts have been reported (11).

Among the ferns, mosses, and lichens, similar distributions are known. In the algae, β-carotene again is the major carotenoid, while lutein is the most commonly encountered xanthophyll.

The third major class of pigments, wholly confined to the

A

B

C

" 3,4-dehydro rhodopi

D

blue-green algae, red algae, and cryptomonads, includes the *phycobilins*—the chromophoric groups of the *phycocyanins* and *phycoerythrins*. The *in vivo* forms, called variously "phycochromoproteins," "bilichromoproteins," "tetrapyrryl-proteins," and, most recently, "biliproteins" (12), yield *in vitro* large protein aggregates which contain firmly bound bile pigments that closely resemble the bilidienes in structure (13). Because of the drastic procedures required to split the chromophoric groups from the protein, it is not certain that the bile pigments obtained are those originally bound in the native functional form. With this reservation, the prosthetic group of phycocyanin appears to be the meso-bilivioline derived by degradation of protoporphyrin IX, i.e., mesobilivioline IX, while that for phycoerythrin is claimed to be mesobilirhodin (see Fig. 3B). It is possible that a fresh approach to the degradation problem, based on partial digestion of the protein component rather than on direct fission of the bile pigment from the protein, will yield unequivocal evidence on the structure of the chromophoric group in the biliproteins.

FIG. 4. Structures of some carotenoids.

A. Manner of isoprenoid unit assembly in carotenoids, according to T. W. Goodwin, *in* "Handbuch der Pflanzenphysiologie" (W. Ruhland, ed.), Vol. 5, p. 394 et seq. Springer, Berlin, 1960.

B. α-Carotene. In β-carotene, double bond is formed between carbons 5 and 6 rather than between carbons 4 and 5, one —H atom is removed from carbon 6 and added to carbon 4 to saturate it. In γ-carotene, bond between carbons 1 and 6 is broken, a double bond is formed between carbons 1 and 2, and one —H atom is removed from carbon 2 and added to carbon 6 to saturate it.

C. Lycopene. For spirilloxanthin, substitute —OCH$_3$ for one —H atom at both carbons 3 and 3'. For lycoxanthin, substitute —OH for one —H atom at carbon 3'. For lycophyll, substitute —OH for one —H atom at both carbons 3 and 3'.

D. The "P 481" group of carotenoids, according to M. Jackman and S. Liane-Jensen, *Acta Chem. Scand.*, 15, 2058 (1961). Shown here is 3,4-dehydrorhodopin. Two other components are anhydrovibrin, in which —OH on carbon 1 is replaced by —OCH$_3$, and rhodovibrin, which is like anhydrovibrin except that the bond between carbons 1' and 2' is saturated and there is an —OH on carbon 1'.

In summary, the only pigment which is certainly common to *all* chloroplasts and grana is chlorophyll *a*. It is also true that there are always a number of accessory pigments present, culled from the other chlorophylls, carotenoids, or biliproteins, but the nature and amounts of these auxiliary components in the photoactive pigment complex is highly variable.

C. Nonphotochemical Components

It is relatively simple to determine the photoactive components in photosynthetically functional particles because these components, which are lipoidal for the most part, remain bound to the subcellular aggregates when caution is taken to preserve photosynthetic activity, as determined by the various partial reactions used to assay chloroplast activity. However, water-soluble components can be lost in varying amounts, depending on the preparative procedures employed during extraction, isolation, and purification.

In the last few years, D. I. Arnon and co-workers have shown that chloroplasts can be prepared which carry out all the essential processes in photosynthesis, and further, that by fractionation procedures, a progressive but controllable loss of the various reactions supported by the whole chloroplasts can be achieved (14). Hence, it is obvious that an exceedingly complex molecular composition, in terms of cofactors, enzymes, and biosynthetic and redox intermediates, must be located in the chloroplast structure. A number of these may prove of crucial importance as obligate participants in the events of the photochemical, as well as of the biochemical, era.

First, there are recent findings relative to the lipid components of chloroplasts, which can account for as much as 40% of the total dry weight of chloroplasts and are essential both as structural and as metabolic factors.

We are far from an adequate biochemical balance sheet for chloroplast lipids, or for the lipids of any cellular structure. It is apparent, however, that while the primary chloroplast lipids are largely uncharged (galactosyl diglycerides)

(15), there are a number of anionic, or zwitterionic, types of special interest, particularly the phosphatides and galactolipids (16, 17). The dominant phosphatide, both in quantity and in metabolic activity, appears to be phosphatidylglycerol (Fig. 5) which can be present in concentrations as high as 10^{-2} M. Some observations on incorporation of $S-^{35}$ labeled into sulfate (18) underscore the possible metabolic role of a new sulfolipid found in chloroplasts of *Scenedesmus*, the structure of which, as given in Fig. 5, indicates it to be a derivative of glucose (19). Of much interest is the observation that although the glycosidic linkage is *alpha*, this ionic glycoside is cleaved by the highly specific *Escherichia coli* β-galactosidase (20).

In runner bean leaves (21), six phosphatides are found, five of which are identified as lecithin, phosphatidylethanolamine, phosphatidylglycerol, phosphatidylinositol, and phosphatidic acid. In addition, there are found four distinct glycolipids, and a fucose-containing sulfolipid which appears to be quite different from the sulfolipid mentioned above as isolated from algae. Lecithinase, the enzyme for degradation of lecithin, is also reported as concentrated in the chloroplast (22). It is apparent that future researches on chloroplast structure and function will lean heavily on knowledge accumulated about lipids as the result of the evolution of increasingly refined analytical techniques, particularly those based on chromatography.

Two other major classes of biochemically important entities occur in chloroplasts and grana. These are the quinoidal compounds (best-known in the form of the naturally occurring naphthoquinones, such as the K vitamins) and the flavines. Little can be said about the latter group except that it appears to be represented by one or more members in any given chloroplast or granum. In higher plants, large amounts of vitamin K_1 (2-methyl-3-phytyl-1, 4-napthoquinone) are found in chloroplasts (23). In addition, some new classes of quinoidal substances, grouped under the generic terms "coenzyme Q" or "ubiquinone," appear to be important constituents of plant and

PHOSPHOLIPIDS

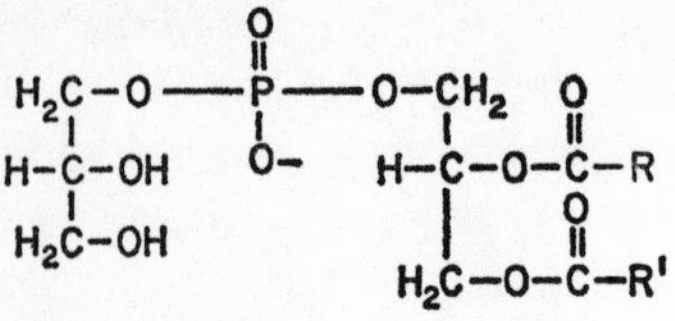

R, R'— Fatty-acid residues

PHOSPHATIDYL GLYCEROL

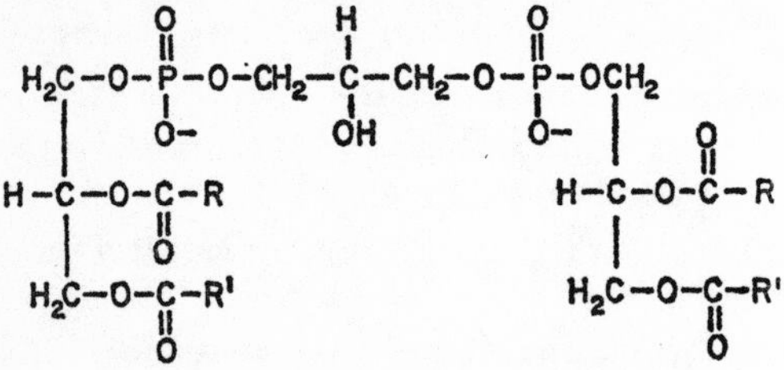

DIPHOSPHATIDYL GLYCEROL ("CARDIOLIPIN")

GALACTOLIPIDS

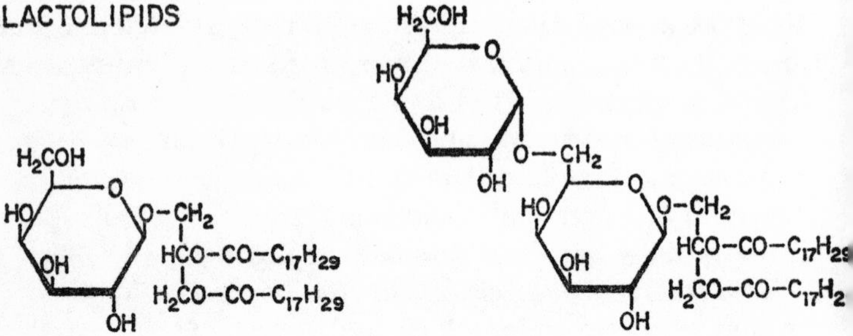

PLANT SULFOLIPID

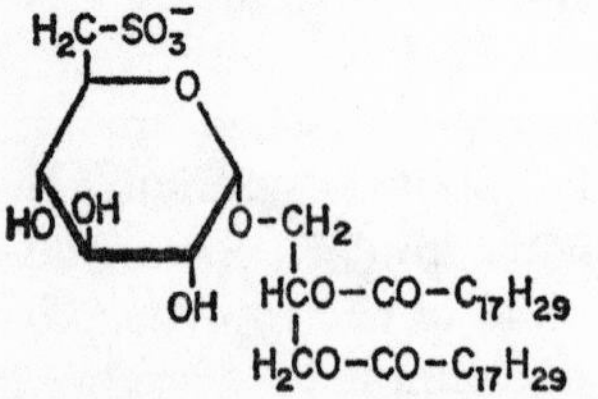

6-SULFO-6-DEOXY-α-D GLUCOPYRANOSYL
DIGLYCERIDE (*)

FIG. 5. Some lipids of the photosynthetic apparatus.

* After H. Daniel *et al.* (quoted by A. A. Benson).

algal chloroplasts (24, 25). These are substituted benzoquinones which often occur in amounts of the same magnitudes as those for the chlorophylls. The characteristic structures for plant ubiquinone—now termed "plastoquinone" (26, 27)—and for coenzyme Q in general (28) are shown in Fig. 6. It will be seen that differences between the various

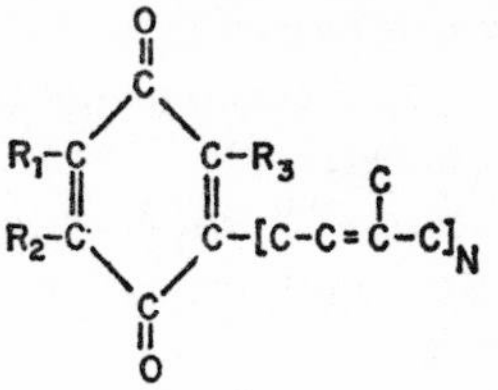

BENZOQUINONES

	R_1	R_2	R_3	N
UBIQUINONE ("CoQ")	OCH_3	OCH_3	CH_3	6-10
PLASTOQUINONE	CH_3	CH_3	H	9
VITAMINS K	HC=C(H)–C(H)=CH		CH_3	4-9

FIG. 6. Quinones of the photosynthetic apparatus.

members of this group lie in the number of isoprenoid residues contained at carbon 6 in the substituent side chain hydrocarbon. The various homologs are named in terms of this number; e.g., Q_{10} represents the coenzyme with the side chain substituent containing ten isoprenoid units (50 carbons). Plastoquinone differs from coenzyme Q, which has a 2,3-dimethoxy-5-methyl-1, 4-benzoquinone nucleus, in that there is no substituent methyl group at carbon 5 and substituents at carbons 2 and 3 are methyl rather than methoxy.

Pyridine nucleotides are present in chloroplasts. Diphosphopyridine nucleotide (DPN) and triphosphopyridine nucleotide (TPN) are found in approximately equal amounts ($1–2 \times 10^{-5}$ *M*) (29), as are enzymes linked to these cofactors, in particular a photoactivated reductase for TPN (30).

The picture for mineral content is quite blurred. Here again, lack of standardization in chloroplast preparations complicates interpretations of results. It seems definite that, in addition to traces of copper, at least two transition metals, iron and manganese, occur, the latter predominantly in free form (31). The available evidence indicates a function for manganese in the oxygen liberation step of photosynthesis (3) (see p. 165). Although some of the iron present is contained in heme protein, particularly cytochromes of a modified c type (see below and p. 35), most is in a bound non-heme form. As in the case of mitochondria, nothing is known about the function of this iron. Copper is found distributed widely in green plant and algal chloroplasts, bound in a protein in which it is capable of reversible oxidation and reduction enzymatically linked to pyridine nucleotides (32, 33). The function of this copper protein—termed "plastocyanin"—remains to be elucidated.

An unusual protein, called "allagochrome," which appears to be functional in photosynthetic phosphorylation by chloroplasts has been reported recently (34).

The fact that heme proteins unique to chloroplasts and grana exist has been known since 1951 when a modified form of cytochrome c, called "cytochrome f," was isolated from leaves of higher plants by R. Hill and R. Scarisbrick (35). In the decade which has elapsed, this fact has assumed an increasing significance for reasons which will be discussed in Chapters III and IV. Here, it may be noted that, whereas the fat-soluble chloroplast components are dominated by tetrapyrrolic chelates of magnesium, the water-soluble components contain large amounts of heme proteins with tetrapyrrolic chelates of iron as prosthetic groups. These heme proteins can account for as much as 10% of the total chloroplast protein. Just as no photosynthetic tissue is known to function without chlorophylls, none is known to function without heme proteins (36).

The major hematin components found in the chloroplasts of green plants, algae, and protozoa are c-type cytochromes. All of these cytochromes are termed, generally, "cytochrome f" (35).

As isolated from leaves of elder or parsley (37), cytochrome f is an acidic protein (isoelectric point ca. pH 4.7) with a molecular weight of approximately 110,000 and two heme prosthetic groups. It is moderately stable to extremes of pH and heat, slowly autoxidizable, and of high oxidizing potential ($E_0' = +0.365$ volts at pH 7). The algal cytochrome *f*, as obtained in crystalline form and high degree of purity from *Porphyra tenera* (38), is a smaller molecule (mol. wt. ca. 13,000) with but one heme prosthetic group, similar in these respects to the classical cytochrome *c*. However, it is acidic (isoelectric point pH 3.5) and has the characteristic high oxidizing potential of plant cytochrome *f* ($E_0' = +0.355$ volts at pH 7). The cytochrome *f* of *Euglena gracilis* appears to be less acidic, showing cathodic electrophoretic mobility at pH 6 according to one investigator (39). In another research (40), a cytochrome *f* of unspecified purity, isolated from apparently the same protozoan strain, differs somewhat in spectroscopic characteristics and has a low, but definitely anodic, mobility at the same pH.

The characteristic pyridine and cyanide hemochromogens of cytochrome *c* can be derived from all specimens of cytochrome *f* found. The location and structure of the "α band" of the reduced heme protein varies, with maxima reported from 552 to 556 mμ. No electrochemical potential lower than $+300$ volts at pH 7 has been observed. Each cytochrome *f* has a characteristic dependence of E_0' on pH (36, 37).

The cytochrome *f* content of green leaf chloroplasts (36), as well as of *Euglena* (33), is given as one mole for every 300–400 moles of chlorophyll.

Another chloroplast hematin component is a cytochrome of the "*b*" type. Much less is known about the distribution and nature of this component in chloroplasts than is the case with *c*–type cytochromes. Examples of chloroplast cytochrome *b*, called "b_6," have been detected in leaves of etiolated barley and other plants (41) but not isolated or solubilized. Its α band absorption maximum in the reduced form is given as 563 mμ. It is rapidly autoxidizable, with E_0' (pH 7) of -0.07 volts, and is present in amounts comparable to cytochrome *f* (41).

Finally, catalase and peroxidase activities appear to be associated with chloroplasts, but no report is available on the purification and characterization of these enzymes as heme proteins. Most significantly (see p. 44), no cytochrome *f* oxidase activity can be detected in chloroplasts (36, 42).

Two kinds of enzymatic activity have been reported in chloroplasts bearing on the *c*-type cytochromes as substrates. One is a particle-bound enzyme which catalyzes photo-oxidation of added cytochrome *c* or cytochrome *f* in the presence of oxygen as "H" acceptor (43, 44). The other is an easily solubilized pyridine nucleotide-linked, flavoprotein, cytochrome *c* reductase (45).

D. Conclusions about Composition in Terms of Known Components

As various workers have emphasized (42, 46, 47), the analytical data available suggest strongly that chloroplasts, as energy storage and energy conversion machines, are analogous to bodies with similar functions in nonphotochemical systems, e.g., the mitochondria of mammalian muscle. Both contain the same types of redox components which can be linked to form an enzyme cycle which mediates biological oxidations coupled to production of intermediates required for biosynthesis. In particular, both accomplish a synthesis of ATP (adenosine triphosphate). In the mitochondrion this process is definitely linked to electron transfer along a chain of cytochromes, flavins, quinones, pyridine nucleotides, etc., and associated enzymes (46)—components which are also found in chloroplasts. Available evidence strongly supports a similar catalytic cycle in chloroplasts (48). The only member of the mitochondrial oxidation chain which is missing from the chloroplast is cytochrome *c* oxidase. On the basis of these analytical results, one may view the chloroplast as similar to a mitochondrion with the important qualification that terminal chemical oxidation is mediated by photoactive components rather than by the classical oxidation catalysts of the mitochondrial type. The chloroplast thus appears as an aggregate of coupled reduction-oxidation systems buried in a matrix of chlorophylls and accessory pigments.

E. Quantum Numbers, Action Spectra, and "Crepuscular Components"

Now I must touch on what is one of the most fascinating, if least understood, aspects of chloroplast chemistry—the existence *in vivo* of short-lived, or chemically labile, compounds made manifest only indirectly by measurements of quantum numbers and action spectra. It is increasingly obvious (see Chapter III) that details of the physics and photochemistry in the interval pt_s 10 to pt_s 4 are inextricably enmeshed with the behavior of labile, uncharacterized entities which one may aptly term "crepuscular components" [4] of chloroplasts.

The number of quanta of any given effective wavelength required to assimilate one mole of carbon dioxide simultaneously with liberation of one mole of oxygen is the *quantum number*. Attempts to determine *the* minimal quantum number in steady-state photosynthesis have caused constant turmoil for well over the last three decades (49). That difficulties should arise in attaining reproducible values for the minimal quantum number (maximal efficiency of energy conversion) is easy to understand on the basis of the natural history of photosynthesis, as presented in Chapter I. Thus, assays of efficiency based on CO_2/O_2 yields require a rigorous correlation between events from pt_s 15 to pt_s 5 and those at pt_s 3 or later, despite the notorious variability of living systems. By expenditure of enormous effort, many highly competent investigators have shown that quantum numbers may be as low as 6, and may even vary down to a much disputed 2.6 (the value for 100% efficiency!). These numbers imply fantastic efficiencies, regardless of which set of values (6–8 or 2.6–3) one credits. The remarkable fact is that, despite the complexity of the photosynthetic process, there is, at the long wavelength

[4] I choose this term to denote entities whose existence is shadowy or fitful, as implied in the French base "crepuscule" (twilight, with the implication of ghostly, evanescent, etc.).

absorption maximum for chlorophyll *a*, a recovery of 25% or more of the absorbed quantum energy as chemical free energy. No comparable storage of energy is known for any photochemical process. Indeed, quantum numbers for non-biological photochemical energy storage normally fall in the range of values many orders of magnitude greater than those found for photosynthesis, whether of the green plant or bacterial types. The conclusion must be drawn that few, if any, dissipative physical or chemical processes intervene between the events in the eras pt_s 15 to pt_s 4 and the reactions in later phases which control carbon dioxide absorption with or without oxygen liberation.

This state of affairs encourages hope that a simple correlation may obtain between the yield of the photochemical process, as determined by some single criterion, such as oxygen liberation, and the wavelength of the absorbed radiation. However, the measurement of the quantitative relation between photochemical yield and number of quanta absorbed at different wavelengths, i.e., the "action spectrum," is not a simple procedure. It is necessary to assure that (*a*) equal amounts of light of different wavelengths are delivered to the system; (*b*) light energies are measured in quantum units, $h\nu$ (numbers of quanta), rather than in terms of total amounts of energy absorbed; (*c*) intensities are well below those required for light saturation at all wavelengths; (*d*) multiple scattering, which accentuates absorption of weakly absorbed radiations as compared with strongly absorbed ones, is minimized. Photosynthetic systems cannot be manipulated in such fashion as to insure that all requirements [(particularly (*d*)] are met completely.

Moreover, inhomogeneities in cellular pigment distribution can effect uncertainties of unknown magnitude. Thus, an overlay of nonphotochemically active absorbing material in the cell wall can filter out radiation which would otherwise be effective if it were to reach the photosynthetic apparatus.

Despite these difficulties, it is often found that over an appreciable range of wavelengths which can be used in photosynthesis, the action spectrum of photosynthesis coincides with the absorption spectrum of the photosynthetically active cellular particle. Usually the action spectrum lies below the absorption curve as the wavelength decreases on the low wavelength side of the Soret peak of chlorophyll. This indicates that nonphotochemically active pigments are responsible for some absorption in the blue and violet.

The question arises as to how quantitative the fit is between action spectra and the absorption spectra of the individual pigments which are assumed to comprise the photoactive complex of the chloroplast. To answer this question, it is necessary to compare the absorption spectra of the chlorophylls, the carotenoids, the biliproteins, etc., under a variety of *in vitro* conditions, with the apparent spectra which may be assigned to the same pigments *in vivo*. Many such studies have been made, particularly in recent years. The results obtained will be presented briefly.

The main red absorption band of all chloroplast-containing systems is quite certainly due to chlorophyll *a*. The characteristic absorption maxima *in vivo*, which lie between 670 and 680 $m\mu$, are displaced from the usual position, 662 $m\mu$, determined *in vitro* with solutions of chlorophyll *a* monomer in ether. It is impractical to work with absorption bands other than those in the red because of interference from absorption by other pigments, particularly carotenoids. Chlorophyll *b*, which has an *in vitro* absorption at 644 $m\mu$, is usually recognizable only as a shoulder at approximately 650 $m\mu$ on the short wavelength side of the chlorophyll *a* band. The shape of the red band varies with different organisms because there are several components present. To distinguish the various *in vivo* pigments, all of which contribute to the red chlorophyll absorption band, a nomenclature is used (50) in which the capital "C" (for chlorophyll) is combined with the suffix "*a*" or "*b*" for the two main chlorophyll forms and with a number which labels the wavelength in millimicrons of the absorption maximum, e.g., C_a673, C_a695, C_a656. Likewise, the letter "P" is used for protochlorophyll, as in P_{650}, P_{635}, etc. It is assumed that all of these pigments are forms of chlorophyll or protochlorophyll, modified by solvation (51), isomerization (52), aggregation (53, 54), crystalline organization (55), binding to specific sites in the chloroplast (50), or surface packing in monomolecular arrays (56). Since the chemical natures of the different moieties responsible for

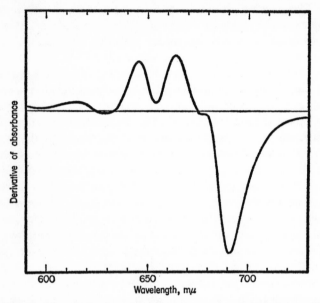

FIG. 7. The derivative absorption spectrum of the green alga, *Chlamydomonas moewusii.* After C. S. French, symposium ref. [7], p. 451. The ordinate is the first derivative of absorbance with respect to wavelength. The peak and trough at 640–660 mμ arise from chlorophyll b; the main trough at ~690 mμ is associated with C_a684, and the shoulder is ascribed to C_a673.

the heterogeneous character of the red chlorophyll band *in vivo* are not known, they may be placed in the category of "crepuscular components," the more so as none survive extraction, except in the form of monomer chlorophyll a.

Two forms, C_a684 and C_a673, are particularly evident in many higher plants and algae (Fig. 7). C_a684 is assumed to be the form which reverts to the classical *in vitro* chlorophyll *a* (absorption maximum 662 mμ) on extraction. Other forms, C_a695 and C_a707, noted in lesser amounts, are also rather widely distributed among plants and algae.

Localization of all these components in chloroplasts is inferred from measurements of action spectra, particularly of "enhancement" effects (see below). Very probably one of the most significant areas of research in photosynthesis has been, and will continue to be, investigations of enhancement phenomena in which quanta of different wavelengths cooperate to raise the quantum yield.

In 1943, R. Emerson and C. M. Lewis (57) found that the energy efficiency of photosynthesis declined more steeply than did the total absorption on the long wavelength side of the red chlorophyll band. This observation was remarkable because it was expected that the energy efficiency should increase as wavelength increased; in other words, there should be no drop-off in *quantum* efficiency anywhere in the whole region of the chlorophyll red band. However, other observers [see, e.g., F. T. Haxo and L. R. Blinks (58)] found very dramatic drop-offs in red algae. Indeed, action spectra were noted (58) in which the maximal efficiency occurred at wavelengths associated with absorption by phycobilins, rather than at wavelengths in regions which corresponded to maximal chlorophyll *a* absorption. Shortly thereafter, O. Warburg and his collaborators reported a remarkable "catalytic" effect of blue light in enhancing quantum yields in the red (59, 60). In fact, they found that practically no photosynthesis occurred at all at the extreme end of the red band region of chlorophyll *a*. This observation has been confirmed numerous times, most recently by J. B. Thomas and Govindjee (61) who reported that in the red alga, *Porphyridium*, there was no demonstrable photosynthesis in the region of longer wavelengths associated with the "5%" tail of chlorophyll *a* absorption, although absorption occurred and enhancement could be observed with radiation at shorter wavelengths.

Emerson (62) and his co-workers, in a continuation of

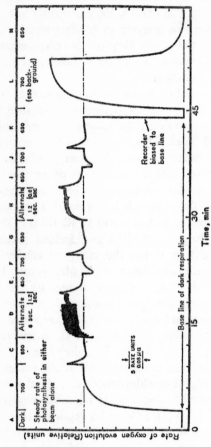

Fig. 8. Emerson enhancement effect for the green alga, *Chlorella pyrenoidosa*. After J. Myers and C. S. French (50). Light of 650 or 700 mμ was adjusted to give equal steady-state rates of oxygen evolution. A "chromatic transient" effect occurs between B and C, E and F, F and G, I and J, and J and K. The Emerson enhancement with both wavelengths given together is shown, at L, by the height of the trace above the dashed line. Enhancement by short period alternation of the two wavelengths, as contrasted with simultaneous presentation, is shown at D and at H.

earlier researches and re-examination of the observations by Warburg and his group, found that while the low photosynthetic efficiency of light on the long wavelength side of the red band could be enhanced and often made maximal by simultaneous absorption of light at shorter wavelengths, the effect required large, rather than catalytic, amounts of supplementary light (63, 64).

An example, taken from work by J. Myers and C. S. French (50), is shown in Fig. 8, wherein it is seen that light at 650 and 700 mμ taken together gives more photosynthesis than the sum of the individual rates. Moreover, and this is extremely important, the two wavelengths *need not be given simultaneously but may be presented alternately*. This means that the photochemical products of the reactions initiated at one wavelength can persist for several seconds, or long enough to interact with those produced in reactions initiated at the other wavelength. From this result, it may be concluded that the radiant free energy absorbed between pt$_8$ 15 and pt$_8$ 9 is stabilized photochemically between pt$_8$ 9 and pt$_8$ 3 with minimal loss by dissipation processes. In Chapter IV I will mention various theories advanced to explain enhancement.

In addition to positive enhancement ("positive Emerson effect"), there is also negative enhancement in which the quantum yield in combined light is lower than in either of the beams taken separately (65). Govindjee (66, 67) has shown that this reversal of the Emerson effect is particularly dependent on both high absolute and high relative intensities of red light. Moreover, it has been shown (68) that extreme red light, in the region 730–770 mμ, can inhibit photosynthesis in the region of the red drop, but not photosynthesis on the short wavelength side of the red band. Just what crepuscular components are present which cause these effects remains to be determined. It may be remarked that W. L. Butler *et al.* (69) have found a photolabile pigment ("phytochrome") which is transformed by illumination with 730 mμ light to another form which absorbs maximally at 660 mμ. This transformation is reversible;

thus, irradiation with 660 mμ light restores the form which absorbs at 730 mμ. It is not certain, however, that this pigment is actually in chloroplasts.

Finally, there are crepuscular components which are noted in examination of photosynthetic tissues by fluorescence, dynamic and flash spectrophotometry. Difference spectra obtained in a variety of ways (oxidation relative to reduction, light relative to dark) appear to implicate crepuscular forms of hematin compounds in addition to pigments. These results will be discussed in Chapter IV.

There is one aspect of the crepuscular problem, as approached by the method of differential absorption in light and dark, that may be considered here. B. Kok and G. Hoch (70) have examined *in vivo* effects at 700 mμ on the basis that the actual converter for the photosynthetic energy storage might absorb maximally in this region of wavelength. They have found that this hypothetical compound, which they call "P_{700}" (not to be confused with P for protochlorophyll, as above), can be increased in amount by processes dependent on light absorption by the accessory pigments, such as phycobilins in blue-green algae and chlorophyll *b* in green plants. There is a delay between illumination and response which indicates mediation by dark reactions. Differential extraction experiments lead to the suggestion that P_{700} is a modified form of chlorophyll *a*, with an apparent midpoint oxidation potential of approximately +0.41 to +0.45, which is pH independent; one-electron transfer appears to be involved as determined by titration against the ferro-ferricyanide couple. Because light bleaches in the same way as does ferricyanide, it is supposed that P_{700} is oxidized in the light and reduced in the dark; thus it can have a function as an oxidase. Similar phenomena have been noted previously by L. N. M. Duysens (71) and J. C. Goedheer (72), and the suggestion that some form of chlorophyll can act as an oxidase in cyclic electron transfer activated by photon absorption has been advanced by these authors as well as by R. Hill (42) and M. D. Kamen (47, 73). The absence of a typical cytochrome oxidase in the photosynthetic apparatus is correlated with such a function for activated chlorophyll.

III. Chloroplast Structure and Development

Of all the topics dealt with in this book, few have been worked over more than chloroplast evolution and organization. It is hopeless to attempt even a brief survey. Until very recently, with the development of the electron microscope and the increase in sophistication about use of mutants and manipulation of biological material, the literature, while enormous, contained little which gave quantitative information about the fine structure of chloroplast systems. The most recent studies have exploited organisms which present unique advantages with regard to size, correlation with growth processes, and biochemical control. For a few of the many reviews available, the reader is referred to articles by H. Leyon (74), R. Sager (75), D. V. Wettstein (76), A. Frey-Wyssling (77), and J. J. Wolken (78).

Studies with both the optical and the electron microscope strongly suggest that the distribution of pigments in the mature chloroplast or granum is heterogeneous, but no good evidence is at hand which provides a detailed map of pigment distribution.

It is not difficult to calculate that the bulk chlorophyll concentration in a chloroplast of one μ diameter is close to 0.01 M. In the event that the chlorophyll is concentrated in localized areas, such as the subchloroplast granum (diameter effectively ca. 0.1 μ or less), the concentration can be of the order 0.1 M, or more. This fact immediately poses questions as to the state of chlorophyll under such dense packing conditions. (This will be considered in Chapter III.) The chemical nature of chlorophyll suggests that it could be concentrated at interfaces between hydrophilic and hydrophobic phases which could be integral parts of lamellar structures such as are often seen in microphotographs of sectioned chloroplasts (see Frontispiece). The lamellar structures are obvious not only in portions of chloroplasts, but also in much smaller grana which are contained in blue-green algae and other microorganisms which do not have chloroplasts. It is of interest that, if it is assumed that all the chlorophyll can be packed into a monomolecular layer with a surface area of approximately one $m\mu^2$ for each chlorophyll, there is just enough room in the lamellae to accommodate the number of chlorophyll molecules found (79). Electron microscopy indicates that lamellar structure develops with formation of chlorophyll (78). Newly synthesized chlorophyll, minus its phytol "tail," is assumed to be absorbed in the precursor bodies which are essentially "structureless." Concomitant with attachment of the tails, layers form and supply interfaces into which chlorophyll is supposed to concentrate. The interfaces are constituted by two lipoprotein layers with lipid sides presented to each other (79a).

Various models have been proposed as a basis for the understanding of chloroplast function in relation to structure (76, 77, 78, 80). At the greatest amplifications available, single lamellae appear as large, flattened, globular structures with pebbled surfaces. Each of the pebbles has an area which could accommodate about 200 chlorophylls stacked together in close array (i.e., ca. 200 $m\mu^2$).

Studies on chloroplast growth appear best prosecuted with microorganisms rather than with higher plants, because the experimenter has more precise control of the developmental processes in the case of the former.

Euglena gracilis, as an example, is a unicellular organism which can be easily manipulated by changes in environmental conditions. It can be grown in a completely synthetic medium, in dark and in light; that is, its growth is not dependent on the absence or presence of chloroplasts. Formation of chlorophyll and chloroplasts takes place only in the light. Loss of chloroplasts and chlorophyll can be induced by a variety of treatments, such as ultraviolet (UV) irradiation, incubation with streptomycin, and culture at elevated ("bleaching") temperatures. Hence, this microorganism is an attractive test object. Studies from two laboratories will be cited as examples.

In the first of these, there is the approach based on correlation between biochemical differentiation, as evidenced by molecular analysis, and morphology. G. Brawerman and E. Chargaff (81), working with etiolated *Euglena*, find that chlorophyll formation ceases abruptly when irradiation ceases, and resumes gradually upon resumption of illumination (Fig. 9). The lag in chlorophyll formation in these resting cells cannot be ascribed to the need for adaptation because they are already fully adapted. Hence it follows that induction by light requires production of certain factors. It is also found that in chloroplast formation, induced by light in resting etiolated cells (82), the appearance of chlorophyll is correlated with a stimulation of ribonucleic acid and protein turnover, accompanied by a shift of proteins from cytoplasm to chloroplast. The immediate cessation of chlorophyll formation when the light is turned off (Fig. 9) leads these workers to the conclusion that the

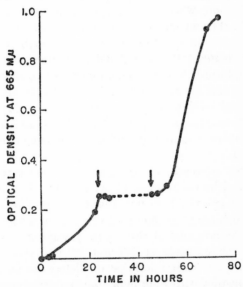

Fig. 9. Effect of interruption of illumination on the formation of chlorophyll in resting *Euglena gracilis*. After G. Brawerman and E. Chargaff (81). Solid line: in light; broken line: in dark. Dark-grown, washed cells were incubated in "resting" medium at room temperature.

factors concerned in chlorophyll formation are labile and in a dynamic state in which they require continuous regeneration. They discard the simple alternative that light is needed as a catalyst because chlorophyll formation can occur in many photosynthetic tissues wholly as a dark process.

Chlorophyll formation in resting cells is relatively unaffected when cells are maintained at temperatures of 34°–35° C. At this temperature, growing cells exhibit a gradual trend to a linear time relation of chloroplast growth which eventually results in a decline in chlorophyll content. The writers interpret the differential responses of resting and growing cells to this bleaching treatment as owing to a block in formation of a catalyst required for chloroplast development.

Analyses of the ribonucleic acids of green and etiolated *Euglena* cells also indicate that significant differences exist at the molecular level in nonphotochemical components, depending on whether chloroplasts are present or absent (83). The green organisms show more adenylic and uridylic acids relative to cytidylic and guanylic acids than do the etiolated cells. Cells that have permanently lost the ability to form chlorophyll because of prolonged heat treatment (34°–35° C) resemble etiolated cells in this respect. Studies such as these may be considered as examples of an approach which can be pursued profitably for elucidation of chloroplast morphology and development at the molecular level.

Another approach of significance for future research is exemplified by the work of H. T. Epstein, H. Lyman, and J. A. Schiff (84–87). They note that UV irradiation at dosage levels which are nonlethal results in cells which form colorless clones incapable of chloroplast formation. The action spectrum shows peaks at 260 and 280 mμ; this fact, combined with the observation that the defect can be abolished by reactivation with blue light (but not red), suggests that self-duplicating units are present as cytoplasmic particles containing nucleic acid which, in some way, mediate chloroplast formation. These results are reminiscent of those quoted above in which a correlation is found between nucleoprotein metabolism and development of chloroplasts.

By exploitation of the fact that red light induces chloroplast formation, but is ineffective in photoreactivation, these workers have been able to separate UV effects on chloroplast development from effects on duplication of chloroplasts. They find that in cells incapable of chloroplast duplication, conversion of protochlorophyll to chlorophyll proceeds normally. By fluorescence microscopy (88), they monitor the appearance of chloroplasts as chlorophyll-containing particles and show that chloroplast development also follows a normal course. Thus, they find that UV irradiation specifically interferes with formation of structures produced in cell division and required for chloroplast formation.

From results obtained by a combination of electron and fluorescence microscopy, these workers have observed the presence of plastid precursors in dark-grown *Euglena,* which appear to be similar to structures found in higher plants. These particles, called "proplastids," are about one μ in diameter; they appear to lengthen upon exposure of the cell to light, and then develop growths ("blebs") off the inner part of a double membrane encasing them. These blebs give rise to full-fledged lamellae which increase in number linearly with time. The rate of appearance of lamellae averages one every six hours in the light after full lengthening of the proplastids. This one-by-one formation of lamellae is not observed in higher plant chloroplasts, where lamellae appear to develop in bunches and replicate in parallel geometric patterns.

IV. Chromatophore Composition

The term "chromatophore," as applied to bacterial subcellular aggregates which contain the entire photoactive pigment complex, seems to have been used first by R. Y. Stanier, A. B. Pardee, and H. K. Schachman (89, 90) in 1952.

These investigators, working with the facultative photo-heterotrophe *Rhodospirillum rubrum,* isolated relatively large particles which appeared in the electron microscope as flattened disks about 100 mμ in diameter. This microorganism—together with the photoanaerobe, *Chromatium*—has been most widely used in studies of chromatophore composition and development (79, 88–97).

Chromatophores, like the parent cells, cannot develop molecular oxygen photochemically. However, they exhibit all the other partial reactions studied in chloroplasts, i.e., photoreduction of pyridine nucleotides coupled to oxidation of hydrogen donors (reduced flavin, succinate, etc.), photophosphorylation, photooxidations with or without concomitant phosphorylation, and pyridine nucleotide reduction coupled to photophosphorylation. The utilization of the bacterial chromatophore may, in future research on minimal photosynthetic structures, provide test objects which possess many advantages over the systems available from plants and algae.

It appears that the most complete quantitative analysis of a photosynthetic system at the molecular level is included in studies of chromatophores and chromatophore fragments of *Chromatium.* J. W. Newton and G. A. Newton (93) examined the properties of these particles as prepared by various fragmentation procedures. Gross composition and characterization of some components were determined as a function of progressive fragmentation. These data apply to washed chromatophores, which are mainly large aggregates present after relatively short periods of cell disruption. A few remarks may be directed at some major aspects of the molecular composition revealed in these studies as characteristic of a structure functionally active in, but not minimal for, photosynthesis.

First, no more than 20 micromoles of the total of 85 micromoles of phosphorus present can be ascribed to nucleic acid. This may be contrasted with tenfold greater magnitudes reported for *R. rubrum* chromatophores. It is to be expected that large variations in molecular composition and nature will occur as the source of the particles changes. This is true for all characteristic components of the photosynthetic apparatus, e.g., chlorophylls (79), carotenoids (11), heme proteins (36), and quinones (25).

Second, the chromatophores are relatively rich in ribonucleic acid (RNA) and poor in deoxyribonucleic acid (DNA) (90), a fact which suggests a gross nucleic acid composition like that of microsomes. The over-all phosphorus distributions in various fractions of silver beet microsomes (98) are much like those found in *Chromatium* (99) chromatophores and in spinach chloroplasts (100).

Table I

MOLECULAR COMPOSITION OF CHROMATIUM CHROMATOPHORES[a]
(Based on one gram wet weight)

Fraction	Weight	Remarks
Protein (mg)	166	Modified biuret assay
Cytochrome (μmole)	0.18 ($\sim$17 mg)	Pyridine hemochromogen assay
Carbohydrate (mg)	62	Anthrone assay
Acid-soluble	5	Mainly as pentose
Insoluble	57	Mainly as galactose polymer
Lipid (mg)	89	Mainly as phosphatidylglycerol (19); only base present: ethanolamine (97)
Pigments (μmoles)	—	—
Bacteriochlorophyll	3.4	Spectrophotometric assay
Carotenoids	1.6	Spectrophotometric assay
Nucleotides (μmoles)	9.5	Assay by ultraviolet absorption as adenine
Pyridine	0.2	Fluorimetric assay of TCA extract
Flavin (μmoles)	0.17	—
Quinone (μmoles)	0.5	Benzoquinone "Q_7" (25)
Phosphate (μmoles)	85	—
Acid-soluble	9.4	8.5 μmoles inorganic phosphorus
Insoluble	73	51 μmoles lipid phosphorus
Iron (μmoles)	12	Mainly as nonheme
Acid-soluble	5	Mainly as ferrous

[a] See Newton and Newton (93), for source of data and analytical procedures.

Third, the major fraction of carbohydrate is polysaccharide, mostly a polymer of galactose. Further fragmentation of these chromatophores to small fragments (ca. 20–50 mμ in diameter) results in loss of practically all this polysaccharide.

Fourth, the only basic lipid present appears to be a cephalin (ethanolamine phosphatidylglycerol).

Fifth, nearly 10% of the total protein is accounted for as the *Chromatium* cytochrome *c* and the "RHP" (*Rhodospirillum* heme protein) variant. Trace amounts of other heme proteins, with associated catalase and peroxidase activities, are present.

In summary, for every 20 bacteriochlorophylls, there are in the chromatophores 11 carotenoids, 1.5 heme proteins, 1 flavin, and 1 pyridine nucleotide. The smaller fragments, derived by further sonication, are enriched in lipid and protein at the expense of polysaccharide. They contain approximately 60% protein and approximately 40% lipid, whereas in chromatophores the protein and lipid contents are approximately 50 and 25%, respectively, with polysaccharide contributing the remainder. In the chromatophore fragments, one finds for every 40 bacteriochlorophylls 17 carotenoids, 3 heme proteins, 0.5 flavin, and 1 pyridine nucleotide. These fragments are depleted systems which require supplementation by supernatant fractions for expression of full photosynthetic activity, as evidenced by capacity for photophosphorylation (101). It is noteworthy that the heme proteins persist in association with bacteriochlorophyll, while other fractions are lost. One sees that, just as in the case of chloroplasts, chromatophores show a molecular make-up characterized by inclusion of components which comprise a typical electron transport chain, supplementary to photoactive pigments.

Some mention of cellular derivatives called "protoplasts" is appropriate. These are cellular structures prepared from bacteria by procedures such as exposure to penicillin or lysozyme in hypotonic sucrose. Such protoplasts have been prepared from *R. rubrum,* e.g., by M. C. Karunairatnam,

J. Spizizen, and H. Gest (102). The spiral-shaped wild-type cells are converted to spherical bodies which appear to contain opaque granules adherent to the inner membrane. These granules contain photoactive pigments and other components of chromatophores, so may represent chromatophores either in their original state or in a stage immediately preceding final separation from cellular material. Protoplast preparations have received relatively little attention as yet, but they may prove helpful in future researches on localization of metabolic systems in photosynthetic and nonphotosynthetic cellular activity.

A short mention of other approaches to chromatophore composition should include disruption by detergents (103) and immunochemical analyses (104–106). C. Bril (103) has demonstrated that chromatophores derived by sonic disruption of *Rhodopseudomonas spheroides,* a facultative photoheterotrophe, show characteristic bacteriochlorophyll absorption spectra, with major peaks at 800 and 850 mμ and a shoulder at 880 mμ. Upon homogenization in "tris" buffer and a nonionic detergent, "Triton X," centrifugal separation yields a soluble fraction devoid of the usual 880 mμ component. This component is recovered in the resuspended sediment. Similar studies with chloroplasts have been reported previously using ionic detergents (10) but with no evidence of such separation of pigment or isolation of crepuscular components. J. W. Newton and L. Levine (104) have found that proteolysis of *Chromatium* chromatophores causes progressive losses of the far infrared component in the multiple peaks of bacteriochlorophyll. This process is semi-reversible; if tryptic digestion has not proceeded too far, it can be reversed quantitatively by addition of a reducing agent, such as cysteine. Newton and Levine (104) and Newton (105) have also reported successful preparation of antisera, obtained by challenging rabbits with injected preparations of purified chromatophores and extracts of dark- and light-grown cells. They have demonstrated the existence of antigenic chromatophore components common to both dark- and light-grown cells, as well as of antigens specific for chlorophyll-containing portions of chromatophores. By means of these test antibodies, Newton has conducted preliminary studies on the kinetics of chromatophore development and dissolution.

J. A. Orlando, L. Levine, and M. D. Kamen (106) have used antisera directed against specific heme proteins of *R. rubrum*, e.g., cytochrome c_2 and RHP, to study the relation between *in vivo* and *in vitro* forms of these proteins (see p. 57). Although there are limitations in the immunochemical approach, these studies suggest that much valuable information can be obtained on chromatophore composition, localization of functional sites, etc. It does not appear that this approach has been attempted with chloroplasts.

V. Individual Components of the Chromatophore

A. *Photoactive Pigments*

The tetrapyrrolic chelates of magnesium of major importance in the photosynthetic bacteria appear to be confined to a few special types, at least so far as *in vitro* forms are concerned. In the purple photosynthetic bacteria, only one form of chlorophyll is extractable. This is called "bacteriochlorophyll" and is a dihydro derivative of chlorin, i.e., a tetrahydroporphyrin. Its currently accepted structure is shown in Fig. 3 (107). In the green photosynthetic bacteria, of which only a few strains are known, there appear to be at least two molecular species, as noted in two different strains of *Chlorobium thiosulfatophilum* (108, 109). Most of the strains available appear to contain exclusively one form (108). This is called "*Chlorobium* chlorophyll-660" because its main absorption band in the red centers at 660 mμ. Although the spectroscopic properties of these chlorophylls [sometimes called "bacterioviridin" (107)] suggest a close resemblance to chlorophyll *a*, A. S. Holt and H. V. Morley (110), as well as R. Y. Stanier and J. H. C. Smith (108), have been unable to obtain a positive Molisch phase test, considered requisite for demonstration of the cyclopentanone ring between carbon γ and carbon 6 so characteristic of chlorophyll *a*. In the "660" form, *Chlorobium* chlorophyll has been examined sufficiently by Holt and Morley (110) to permit the conclusion that a partial structure of the type shown in Fig. 3 can be suggested, in which ethyl groups occupy substituted positions at carbons 2 and 4, with the very novel suggestion of a normal propyl group at carbon 6. The presence of a conjugated keto group is also inferred, but its location is unknown.

The carotenoid mixtures which may be inferred as present in various bacterial chromatophores are summarized in Table II. The structural formulae for some of these carotenoids will be found in Fig. 4. Observations corresponding to those tabulated may be extended to two species of the green photosynthetic sulfur bacteria (112) to show that, insofar as certain strains are concerned (*Chlorobium limicola, Chlorobium thiosulfaticum,* and an unidentified halophilic species), they are unique in their carotenoid distributions, which are wholly different from those observed in the purple photosynthetic bacteria. Thus, the major component in all of these strains of green sulfur bacteria is γ-carotene. Another component present in some instances is the 3-hydroxy derivative of carotene, called "rubixanthin." Traces of pro-γ-carotene are noted in all cases examined.

B. *Nonphotoactive Components*

The quinoidal components of chromatophores differ from those of chloroplasts. In general, they are not naphthoquinones, such as the K vitamins. They resemble closely the plastoquinones of chloroplasts, in that they are substituted benzoquinones; however, they contain different substituents, namely, methoxy groups in place of methyl, and methyl groups in place of hydrogen, i.e., 2,3-dimethoxy-5-methyl-1,4-benzoquinone (see schematic representation in Fig. 6). The characterization by the carbon 6 side chain isoprenoid residue number, followed for plastoquinones, is retained for the chromatophore "ubiquinones," also called

Table II

CAROTENOID DISTRIBUTION IN PURPLE PHOTOSYNTHETIC BACTERIA[a]

Bacterium	Lycopene	"P481"	"Y"	Spheroidenone	Spirilloxanthin[c]	Lycoxanthin[d]	OH-"P481"	OH-"Y"	OH-"P512"	OH-Spheroidenone	Desmethyl-spirilloxanthin
Rhodopseudomonas capsulatus	+	−	+	+	−	−	−	+	−	+	−
Rhodopseudomonas gelatinosa	?	−	+	+	+	−	−	+	+	+	−
Rhodopseudomonas palustris	+	+	−	−	+	+	+	−	−	−	+
Rhodopseudomonas spheroides	+	−	+	+	?	−	−	+	−	+	−
Rhodospirillum rubrum	+	+	−	−	+	+	+	−	−	−	+
Rhodospirillum molischianum	+	−	−	−	−	+	+	−	−	−	−
Rhodospirillum photometricum	+	++	−	−	−	++	++	−	−	−	?
Chromatium	+	++	−	−	+	+	?	−	−	−	−

[a] See T. W. Goodwin (111).

[b] Symbols: + present; − absent; ? traces.

[c] Also known as "rhodoviolascin."

[d] The dihydroxy derivative of lycopene, called "lycophyll," has also been reported present in *Chromatium* [see C. R. Benedict, R. C. Fuller, and J. A. Bergeron, *Biochim. et Biophys. Acta*, **54**, 525 (1961)].

"Q" coenzymes. Thus, in *Chromatium,* the quinone present in large amounts, as mentioned previously, is Q_7, i.e., the coenzyme Q with side chain at carbon 6 containing seven isoprenoid residues.[5] In *R. rubrum,* the chromatophores exhibit very large amounts of Q_9—where the side chain substituent possesses nine isoprenoid residues. Rudney (113) has presented some preliminary data which appear to implicate Q_7 as an intermediate in photophosphorylation.

The nature of lipid components of chromatophores, so far as they have been studied, appears to resemble somewhat that of chloroplast lipids. Thus, phospholipids and sulfolipids appear to be characteristic (17, 19). 1,3-Diglycerophosphorylglycerol is observed (114). In *R. rubrum* chromatophores, the following components have been noted (composition based on packed volume $\pm20\%$): phosphatidylglycerol, $5 \times 10^{-3}M$; phosphatidylethanolamine, $2 \times 10^{-3}M$; diphosphatidylglycerol, $8 \times 10^{-4}M$; phosphatidylinositol, $2 \times 10^{-4}M$ (A. A. Benson, private communication).

Little is known about the nature of chromatophore flavins and pyridine nucleotides other than that they are present and functionally active (115, 115a).

The hematin compounds of chromatophores have been studied extensively (36). Speculations about their role in bacterial photosynthesis are not confined to the obvious one of participation in electron transport coupled to photophosphorylation, but also include a primary role in the photochemical era (47). Data relevant to these aspects of heme protein function will be discussed in the following chapters.

The major soluble heme protein components of bacterial chromatophores are modified *c*-type cytochromes (36). Considerable variations in midpoint oxidation potentials, in responses of redox potentials to changes in pH, and in physiochemical constants are found when the *c*-type cyto-

[5] Recently, R. C. Fuller *et al.* (112a) have reported the presence of vitamin K in considerable quantity (1.9 μmoles/gm dry weight) in *Chromatium* chromatophores.

chromes from different photosynthetic bacteria are compared (36). The range of physiochemical characteristics is
as wide as in the f cytochromes. Thus, the c-type cytochrome
of *R. rubrum* is a small heme protein (mol. wt. ca. 12,000)
with one heme prosthetic group, an isoelectric point on the
acid side (pH 6.4), and a midpoint potential at pH 7 of
340 millivolts (115). The c-type cytochrome of *Chromatium*
is a large heme protein (mol. wt. ca. 95,000) with three heme
groups, an isoelectric point at pH 5.5, and a midpoint
potential (pH 7) of 10 millivolts (116).

The amino acid compositions of these two c-type cytochromes have been determined (117, 118). The data show
that the chromatophore cytochromes of the c-type, as well
as those isolated from some chemosynthetic anaerobes, are
similar to the classical horse heart cytochrome c, in that
they have large amounts of lysine (17–20 residues/heme)
in addition to at least two histidine and two cysteine residues. Acidic properties are correlated with the presence
of the dicarboxylic amino acids, aspartic and glutamic,
sufficient in number to more than compensate for the basic
amino acids present. A heme peptide has been derived
from *R. rubrum* cytochrome c which contains the same
sequence of amino acids around the heme binding site as is
characteristic of all c-type cytochromes derived from a
variety of aerobic mammalian and microbial tissues (119).
Thus, two cysteinyl residues separated by two amino acid
residues with a vicinal histidinyl residue are present. The
cysteinyl residues are bound by thioether linkages to the
vinyl side chains of heme.

A few b-type cytochromes have been detected in chromatophores but only in those derived from the facultative
photoheterotrophes (120). One such heme protein—a poly-
meric b-type from *Rhodopseudomonas spheroides*—has been
prepared in soluble form (121).

A variant heme protein, present in amounts comparable
to the c-type cytochromes (122, 36), has been found in the
chromatophores of the purple photosynthetic bacteria. This
hematin compound, called "RHP" (abbreviated from

"*Rhodospirillum* heme protein" (123)), is a hybrid form of cytochrome with properties partly of cytochrome *b*, partly of cytochrome *c*, and partly of myohematin-type proteins. As isolated from *R. rubrum* in pure crystalline form, it has a molecular weight of 28,000, two heme groups, an isoelectric point at pH 4.3, and a midpoint potential at pH 7 of −8 millivolts (115). The same type of protein obtained from *Chromatium* (116) has very similar properties (mol. wt. 35,000, two heme groups, isoelectric point at pH 5.5, and midpoint potential at pH 7 of −5 millivolts).

The spectrochemical properties of RHP are most unusual. Its spectrum is that of an alkaline peroxidase, with absorption maximum for the reduced form showing two components in the Soret region at 423 and 430 mμ. The α band of the reduced form is heterogeneous, with distinct, but not well-resolved, maxima at 547 and 565 mμ. The heme groups cannot be split by cold acetone-acetic acid mixtures, as in the protoheme enzymes (hemoglobin, catalase, peroxidase, cytochrome *b*), but are removed only by drastic procedures, as in the case of cytochrome *c*. Treatment with strong acid or sodium amalgam gives products identical with those derived from cytochrome *c*. The pyridine and cyanide hemochromogens formed from RHP are also identical spectroscopically with those obtained from cytochrome *c*. RHP is autoxidizable; it combines in the reduced (ferrous) form with carbon monoxide and with nitric oxide in both reduced and oxidized forms (115b), but with no other ligand either in the oxidized or in the reduced form. It is completely reduced by dithionite or by the hydrogen-palladium couple, but incompletely by ascorbate. In the reduced form it can couple directly with cytochrome *c*, reducing the latter completely, as is to be expected from its electrochemical potential. Its possible function as an oxidase has been discussed elsewhere (36, 123a).

Both catalases and peroxidases exist in chromatophores. The catalase of *Chromatium* has been partially purified and characterized as a protoheme enzyme (124).

The presence of the cytochrome photooxidase and flavin-mediated cytochrome reductase, enzymes mentioned previously as present in chloroplasts, is also noted in chromatophores (125). A very weak, cyanide-sensitive oxidase is found, associated apparently with the carbon monoxide-binding pigment present. The possible identity with RHP has not been substantiated. Evidence accumulated so far (126) supports the notion that in chromatophores as well as in chloroplasts, pyridine nucleotides, quinones, flavins, heme protein reductases and heme proteins form part of a chain which mediates electron transport coupled to phosphorylation—the whole aggregate summing to the process of photophosphorylation.

C. More Quantum Numbers, Action Spectra, and "Crepuscular Components"

The absorption spectra of the photoactive pigment complex in chromatophores differ greatly from those for the isolated *in vitro* forms of bacteriochlorophyll and *Chlorobium* chlorophylls. E. C. Wassink *et al.* (127) and C. S. French (128) noted many years ago that the absorption maxima which could be ascribed to *in vivo* bacteriochlorophyll in the purple photosynthetic bacteria (e.g., 890, 850, and 800 mμ peaks) were fused and shifted to one broad band with maximum absorption at approximately 778 mμ when the pigment was extracted and purified in organic solvents. In *Chlorobium*, the *in vivo* absorption maximum at 740 mμ corresponded to an *in vitro* form with absorption maximum at 665 mμ.

These dramatic shifts toward the blue, which amount to as much as 100 mμ difference between *in vivo* and *in vitro* forms, are characteristic only of chromatophore chlorophylls. Relatively minor blue shifts are seen in chloroplast chlorophylls. Although the absorption intensities as well as locations of absorption maxima vary considerably from one bacterial species to another, only the one bacteriochlorophyll with the broad absorption peak at 778 mμ appears on extraction. Relative heights of absorption maxima for *in vivo* forms can be altered in any single chromatophore by manipulation of cultural environment. Katz and Wassink also showed (129) that the various absorption maxima responded differently to heat and pH.

The various bacteriochlorophyll types present *in vivo* are termed "B890," "B850," and "B800" following a convention established by L. N. M. Duysens (130). This terminology, based wholly on location of infrared absorption peaks, can be extended to bacteriochlorophyll types which may be present in bacteria other than those investigated to the present.

Explanations have been advanced to account for these phenomena based on assumptions that (*a*) one pigment is present, bound to three different sites; (*b*) one pigment is present but exhibits three separate optical transitions arising from perturbations induced at a single binding site; (*c*) one pigment is present in varying states of aggregation (131). Attempts to separate the three moieties present and to exhibit them in *in vitro* form have been only partially successful (103, 104, 132).

Extensive investigations on the spectroscopic and redox properties of bacteriochlorophyll *in vivo* and *in vitro* have been published by J. C. Goedheer (133, 134) and L. N. M. Duysens (71). Bacteriochlorophyll dissolved in organic solvents (methanol, acetone, benzene, ether, etc.) can be bleached by irradiation with infrared light. An example of such an effect is given in Fig. 10. Similar effects are obtained by incubation with oxidants (ferric chloride, ferricyanide, permanganate, etc.) from which an apparent midpoint oxidation potential of +0.4 to +0.47 volt can be assigned. The effect can be reversed by addition of a reducing agent. E. Rabinowitch and J. Weiss, it should be noted, found similar effects with chlorophyll *a* (135) many years previously.

There is a tendency to leap to the conclusion that *in vivo* light bleaching is, in effect, the result of oxidation (71). However, many alternative explanations can be offered. One is that, in the *in vivo* bleaching process, a compound other than the pigment is oxidized and that this influences

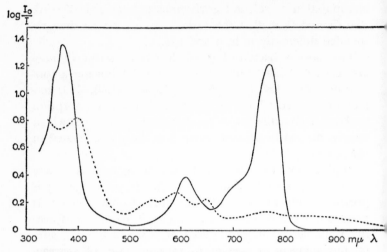

FIG. 10. Absorption spectrum of bacteriochlorophyll from *R. rubrum*, dissolved in methanol. After J. C. Goedheer (133). Dotted line shows pigment after exposure to high intensity light adsorbed mainly in the infrared.

the position of energy levels in the bacteriochlorophyll molecule, particularly if the oxidized moiety is in a protein or other entity binding the bacteriochlorophyll. Another possibility is that bleaching occurs by *reduction* of the bacteriochlorophyll. Reduction of chlorophylls, as shown so exhaustively by A. A. Krasnovskii and his collaborators (see p. 156), exhibits the bleaching effect. An interesting finding is that only the 890 mμ band of the *in vivo* pigment complex can be bleached reversibly (133). This correlates with the observations by C. Bril (103) and by J. W. Newton and L. Levine (104), who also noted a differential sensitivity of this component to detergent action and proteolysis.

By studies on dichroism, exhibited in oriented pigment systems, and from measurements on polarization of fluorescence in solutions of pigments, J. C. Goedheer (134, 137) deduced that (*a*) absorption of quanta in the region 400–750 mμ occurred in the plane of the porphyrin heads, rather than perpendicular to the plane, when the pigments were oriented by pressure between glass plates in lecithin or ammonium oleate, and (*b*) the optical transition correlated with the 590 mμ absorption band was perpendicular in its mode of oscillation to that responsible for the 780 mμ band.

In Chapter III, the conclusions to be derived from measurements of this type will be discussed again. At this point it suffices to mention that determinations by absorption and fluorescence spectroscopy are vital in advancing knowledge on the structural conditions which can give rise to the *in vivo* modifications of the chromatophore pigments.

Few data are at hand on the presence or absence in chromatophores of enhancement by quantum cooperation ("Emerson effect"). One preliminary study by J. M. Olson (138) shows that the quantum efficiency for photophosphorylation by *R. rubrum* chromatophores is the same ($\pm 10\%$) for light at wavelengths on either side of the infrared maximum absorption band (880 mμ); that is, no drop-off is found at 896 mμ relative to efficiency at 862 mμ. A similar result appears to hold for the photoinduced oxidation of the cytochrome system in *Chromatium* chromatophores (139). Thus it appears that in the chromatophore— a system which does not produce molecular oxygen—no Emerson effect exists. This finding, if substantiated, is of fundamental importance in that it establishes a qualitative difference at the photochemical level between the two kinds of photosynthesis—plant and bacterial. Quantum numbers for carbon dioxide assimilation by photosynthetic bacteria do not reveal such a difference. These are found to fall in the same range (6–8) as most such yields for plant photosynthesis (49).

VI. Chromatophore Development

Studies on the natural history and differentiation of chromatophores are only in the most preliminary stages. This can be understood when it is remembered that functional chromatophores can be as small as 20 mμ in diameter. Thus, only with the advent of the electron microscope has a possibility existed for visualization of such bodies. A. W. Frenkel and D. D. Hickman (92) have reported most extensively on the developing structure of chromatophores as seen at various periods of growth of *R. rubrum*. They find that very young cells (ca. 12 hours old) contain no mature chromatophores, but only small cytoplasmic granules which may be precursor bodies. Lamellar organization of the chromatophores seems to occur only in relatively aged cultures (ca. 8 days), while the unstructured spherical bodies, identified as chromatophores, arise any time after approximately 12 hours. There is a possibility that chromatophores originate at the inner membrane and, in the early stages of formation, exist as linear bodies attached like lamellae to this membrane; thus, the spherical bodies released into cytoplasm and thence into culture fluids by disruption may be artifacts which result from a rolling-up of membrane fragments released by cellular disruption.

Further insights into chromatophore development come from application of immunochemical procedures, as mentioned previously in the discussion of characterization of chromatophore components. J. W. Newton (94), using antisera derived by injection into rabbits of antigenic extracts from both light-grown and dark-grown *R. rubrum*, has shown that, when light-grown *R. rubrum* is placed in the dark for a short time, a progressive and rapid alteration of cellular components takes place, such that the antigenic bodies which formerly bound bacteriochlorophyll no longer exist—that is, antibodies specific for the chlorophyll-containing antigens of light-grown cells fail to produce pigmented precipitates. This result suggests disorganization of the photosynthetic apparatus in the dark, and may serve as a basis for rationalization of induction phenomena noted when cells are returned to a photosynthetic mode of growth.

More recently, J. W. Newton (140) has shown that chemical scission of disulfide bonds [by treatment with alkaline sulfite in the presence of Cu^{++} or other heavy-metal ions

(141, 142)] as well as sonication, releases serologically active material which is univalently antigenic to the antibodies specific for chlorophyll-binding ("chromatophore-specific") antigens mentioned as obtained in previous researches (94). The inference derived from these studies is that chromatophore antigens are inserted as repeating units between sites defined by S—S bonds. Studies of this type, combined with electron and fluorescence microscopy, can be expected to figure prominently in future researches on chromatophore development.

Perhaps the most remarkable finding with regard to chromatophore development is that of J. Lascelles (143), who has shown that although air suppresses bacteriochlorophyll synthesis in *R. rubrum*, cells grown under strictly dark, aerobic conditions, which are thus rendered devoid of bacteriochlorophyll, nevertheless can initiate bacteriochlorophyll synthesis if the oxygen tension is low, *even in the absence of light.* Apparently, a light-dependent system for pigment synthesis is not needed in chromatophores, in contrast with chloroplasts (see p. 47).

VII. Remarks *in Extenso* on the Fine Structure of the Photosynthetic Apparatus

The two questions posed at the beginning of this chapter may be re-examined now in the light of the brief survey on the molecular compositions and structural aspects of the photosynthetic apparatus which have been presented.

First, with regard to the question of the total composition of the "simplest" photoactive structure, it is apparent that present knowledge provides only an indication of what may constitute the molecular recipe for a minimal structure. Nevertheless, enough is known to state with certainty that a combination of chlorophylls, as essential ingredients, and accessory pigments, the nature of which may vary considerably, are required for maximal efficiency in the quantum-trapping and energy conversion mechanism. In addition, components such as flavins, cytochromes, pyridine nucleotides, and enzymes associated with functional involvement of these moieties must be present, presumably to carry the process from pt_s 4 onward to the final stages of biosynthesis. Definitive data would seem to necessitate analysis of the photosynthetic apparatus at different stages of development from proplastid, or precursor bodies, to the finished structure. This approach should be possible by exploitation of the mutant strains of various algae and protozoa in which chloroplast development is blocked at different parts of the development process. Comparisons could also be made between the chromatophore and chloroplast to yield possible clues as to the nature of mechanisms present in the chloroplast and absent (or inhibited) in the chromatophore, which make possible the evolution of oxygen.

The needed insights into the orientation and placement of vital components in the photosynthetic apparatus require intensive development of a variety of techniques, as well as new approaches as yet undisclosed. Techniques, such as those based on the use of the polarization microscope (77, 144), the electron microscope, and other visualization procedures, are basic but reveal only gross features of structure. Greater resolution (down to a few angstroms) is needed. The possibility of application of X-ray diffraction methods is not as yet in sight. Such methods require test systems ordered sufficiently to distinguish repeating units unambiguously and of a size much smaller than the smallest functional unit available from photosynthetic systems. The major techniques, now applicable, are based on the phenomena of dichroism, birefringence, and polarization of fluorescence.

Dichroism arises from anisotropy of absorption. One of the best test systems offered so far is the giant chloroplast of *Mougeotia*. Electron micrographs of this plate-shaped body reveal lamellae with thickness of approximately 120 Å (80, 145). Such a chloroplast is large enough, so that if it is oriented with its major axis perpendicular to the line of vision, its absorption as a single unit can be measured. Such measurements (134) reveal the *Mougeotia* chloropast structure as consistent with the presence of alternating lamellae with varying refractive indices; each lamellar layer is thin compared with the wavelength of light absorbed.

Dichroism in nonpigmented systems can arise not only because of molecular order ("intrinsic birefringence"), but also because of the presence of layered arrays ("morphic birefringence").[146] For the conditions prevailing in the *Mougeotia* chloroplast (layer thickness $\ll$ wavelength), the relation between the refractive indices of two kinds of layers assumed to be present (n_A and n_B) and their relative thickness, d_A and d_B (defined so that $d_A + d_B = 1$), requires measurement of the refractive index, n_{PAR}, when the electric vector of the incident light is parallel to the layers, and of n_{PERP}, when it is perpendicular (145). The difference in these two indices ($n_{PERP} - n_{PAR}$), is the morphic birefringence; for small values, it is given (134) by expression (A)

$$n_{PERP} - n_{PAR} = 2d_A d_B (n_A - n_B)^2 / n_M \qquad \text{(A)}$$

where n_M is an averaged refractive index for the two kinds of layer. Thus, the variation of the measured morphic birefringence with the difference in refractive indices of the lamellae exhibits a parabolic curve. Because, by convention, the sign of the birefringence is taken as positive when $n_{PAR} > n_{PERP}$, the morphic birefringence of lamellar structures is always negative.

Experimentally, morphic birefringence is shown in two ways. First, chloroplasts are treated with liquids which, by imbibition, diminish the differences in the refractive indices of the layers. Second, the chloroplasts can be plasmolyzed by immersion in concentrated sucrose solutions (147). If the layers are predominantly protein in one type and lipid in the other, the dehydration effected will increase the refractive index of the protein layers as compared to that of the lipid layers. Experimentally, the morphic birefringence is seen to decrease and even to change sign. The decrease results presumably because *in vivo* the refractive index of the lipid layers initially exceeds that of the protein layers. The positive birefringence probably comes from orientation of molecules in the lipid layers in the direction of the optic axis which contributes sufficiently to the absorption so that the negative birefringence, if sufficiently small to begin with, is more than compensated.

Intrinsic birefringence ("dichroism of shape") results when pigments are present in either or both of the two layer systems. If it is assumed that only one layer is pigmented, the birefringence, which in this case is the difference in absorption for the two directions of vibration of the electric vector in the incident light, is given (134) by expression (B)

$$e_{PAR} - e_{PERP} = d_A n_A e_A [1/n_{PAR} - (1/n_{PERP})(n_{PERP}/n_A)^4] \qquad (B)$$

where e_{PAR} and e_{PERP} are the absorption coefficients in the two directions of vibration, and n_A, n_B, and d_A have the same meanings as in expression (A). The birefringence is taken as positive if the absorption in the plane parallel to the optic axis is greater than in the plane perpendicular to the optic axis. It can be shown that the sign of the intrinsic birefringence, unlike that for morphic birefringence, depends on the relative values of n_A and n_B.

Another effect—anomalous dispersion—is expected in regions of maximal absorption when pigments are present. Experimentally, this appears as a marked change in morphic birefringence throughout the wavelength region which brackets the absorption band.

Results from a study of *Closterium* chloroplasts were reported first by W. Menke (144), who noted a weak dichroism. J. C. Goedheer (134) has presented the most extensive researches, in this case with *Mougeotia* chloroplasts. His analysis shows that a picture consistent with the dichroism observed is one in which chlorophyll molecules are close packed and have appreciable orientation in thin layers situated between the two kinds of lamellar structures, one kind primarily protein in nature, the other lipid. Interpretation of the effects is complicated by the simultaneous occurrence of morphic birefringence, together with dichroism which arises from orientation of both chlorophyll and lipid molecules. Variations correlated with aging chloroplasts are found to be explicable in terms of increased chlorophyll *b* content with age.

These conclusions bear strongly on the interpretation of the results expected when the polarization of fluorescence emitted by chloroplasts is studied. If, in the situation of close-packing in thin layers deduced from the results on dichroism, chlorophyll molecules are oriented at random, then one can expect complete depolarization of light emitted as fluorescence. This follows from considerations to be reviewed in Chapter III. A measurable polarization of fluorescence from chloroplasts will indicate some preferential stacking of the chlorophylls. Goedheer (134) has applied this method to a variety of photosynthetic systems. In general, intact cells scatter light and give rise to so much internal reflection that no significant measurements on polarization can be made. With suspensions of *Aspidistra* species, which are transparent, small degrees of polarization can be detected. The same is true of intact cell suspensions of photosynthetic bacteria. In particular, it is noted that in *Chromatium* the same degree of polarization is found in fluorescence at approximately 900 mμ, whether excitation takes place at 800, 850, or 890 mμ (the characteristic absorption maxima of bacteriochlorophyll). This result shows that all three components have the same average orientation in the chromatophore. In the region of carotenoid absorption, no polarization of fluorescence results. This observation can be understood as a consequence either of nonorientation of carotenoids, or of orientation in a direction different from that of the bacteriochlorophylls. Negative polarization effects are found when light is absorbed at 590 mμ because the light in this case is absorbed by an oscillating dipole vibrating in a plane perpendicular to the oscillator responsible for fluorescence.

R. A. Olson, W. L. Butler, and W. H. Jennings (148) have presented the most recent evidence in studies of polarized fluorescence which they have found to occur in the far red (700–740 mμ) when *Euglena* chloroplasts were irradiated with unpolarized light of wavelengths $\geq$ 436 mμ. The effects observed by photography in the region 690–710 mμ were obtained only with chloroplasts viewed on edge, as contained in intact *Euglena gracilis*. Maximum extinction was found when the plane of vibration of the analyzer Nicol prism was parallel to the plane of the lamellae. Dichroic ratios* appeared greater than 4, which is a very large value.

By extension from the studies cited previously on chlorophyll *a*, the absorption band of this "oriented" chlorophyll (on the long wavelength side of the main absorption band) results from a "π-π" transition (see p. 96), in which the electric vector of the molecular oscillator lies in the plane of the porphin ring. Hence, it is concluded that the porphin rings lie in the same plane as the lamellae. These results indicate clearly that a large measure of orientation has been missed in previous studies because the component involved fluoresced in the far red part of the spectrum, which could not be studied because adequate instrumentation was not available.

Most studies based on measurements of dichroism and polarizations of fluorescence have been confined to model systems so far (134, 149). A great accumulation of data and knowledge is available for interpretation of effects observed in chloroplasts and chromatophores, but successful application may be delayed until better test systems than those tried heretofore are available. In the next two chapters there will be considered briefly, among other things, the various aspects of dichroism and fluorescence parameters as they help to elucidate the eras from pt_s 15 to pt_s 4, and an

---

* Defined as the ratio of absorption coefficients for radiation with its electric vector parallel and perpendicular to the symmetry axis of the system.

attempt will be made to delineate major features of the picture which is emerging from the present welter of speculation about the primary process in photosynthesis.

References*

1. See J. B. Thomas, general ref. II, p. 511 et seq.
2. R. M. Leech and R. J. Ellis, *Nature* 190, 790 (1961).
3. See K. A. Clendenning, general ref. II, p. 736 et seq.
4. T. Punnett, *Plant Physiol.* 34, 283 (1959).
5. R. B. Woodward, *Angew. Chem.* 72, 651 (1960).
6. A. S. Holt and H. V. Morley, *Can. J. Chem.* 37, 507 (1959).
7. A. S. Holt, *Can. J. Botany* 39, No. 2,327 (1961).
8. J. H. C. Smith, *Arch. Biochem.* 9, 449 (1948).
9. M. Nishimura and H. Fujishige, *J. Biochem.* (Japan) 46, 225 (1959).
10. D. N. Kupke and C. S. French, general ref. II, p. 394 et seq.; see also L. Bogorad, symposium ref. [5], p. 227 et seq.; and J. H. C. Smith, *ibid.*, p. 257 et seq.
11. For a full account, cf. T. W. Goodwin, general ref. II, p. 394 et seq.
12. C. O'hEocha, *Arch. Biochem. Biophys.* 73, 207 (1958); also symposium ref. [5] p. 181 et seq.
13. R. Lemberg and J. W. Legge, "Hematin Compounds and Bile Pigments," pp. 118ff. Wiley (Interscience), New York, 1949.
14. See D. I. Arnon, general ref. II, p. 773 et seq.
15. A. A. Benson, J. F. G. H. Wintermans, and R. Wiser, *Plant Physiol.* 34, 315 (1959).
16. E. W. Putman and W. Z. Hassid, *J. Am. Chem. Soc.* 76, 2221 (1954).
17. A. A. Benson, symposium ref. [7], p. 392 et seq.
18. M. L. Ibanez and E. S. Lindstrom, *Biochem. Biophys. Research Communs.* 1, 224 (1959).
19. A. A. Benson, *Proc. 5th Natl. Congr. Biochem., Moscow, 1961,* Symposium VI, in press.
20. J. Shibuya, quoted in ref. (19).
21. M. Kates, *Biochem. et Biophys. Acta* 41, 315 (1960).
22. M. Kates, *Can. J. Biochem. Physiol.* 32, 571 (1954).
23. H. Dam, J. Glavind, and N. Nielsen, *Z. physiol. Chem.* 265, 86 (1940).
24. R. A. Morton, *Nature* 182, 1764 (1958).
25. R. L. Lester and F. L. Crane, *J. Biol. Chem.* 234, 2169 (1959).

* Complete information pertaining to symposium references [1] to [7] and general references I, II, and III can be found in Section VI (collateral Reading) of Chapter I.

26. N. R. Trenner, B. H. Arison, R. E. Erickson, C. H. Shunk, D. E. Wolf, and K. Folkers, *J. Am. Chem. Soc.* **81**, 2026 (1959).
27. M. Kofler, A. Langemann, R. Rüegg, U. Gloor, U. Schwieter, J. Würsch, O. Wiss, and O. Isler, *Helv. Chim. Acta* **42**, Part II, 2252 (1959).
28. B. O. Linn, N. R. Trenner, C. H. Shunk, and K. Folkers, *J. Am. Chem. Soc.* **81**, 1263 (1959).
29. D. G. Anderson and B. Vennesland, *J. Biol. Chem.* **207**, 613 (1954).
30. A. San Pietro and H. M. Lang, *Science* **124**, 118 (1956).
31. H. A. Tanner, T. E. Brown, H. C. Eyster, and R. W. Treharne, *Ohio J. Sci.* **60**, 231 (1960).
32. S. Kato, *Nature* **186**, 533 (1960); also S. Kato and A. Takamiya, *ibid.* **189**, 665 (1961).
33. S. Kato, J. Shiratori, and A. Takamiya, *J. Biochem. (Japan)* **51**, 32 (1962).
34. H. B. Habermann, symposium ref. [5], p. 73 et seq.; also H. B. Habermann and A. R. Krall, unpublished data.
35. R. Hill and R. Scarisbrick, *New Phytol.* **50**, 98 (1951).
36. M. D. Kamen, *in* "Enzymes: Units of Biological Structure and Function," (O. H. Gaebler, ed.), pp. 483ff. Academic Press, New York, 1956.
37. H. E. Davenport and R. Hill, *Proc. Roy. Soc.* **B139**, 327 (1952).
38. S. Kato, *J. Biochem. (Japan)* **46**, 629 (1959); see also *Plant and Cell Physiol. (Japan)* **1**, 91 (1960).
39. M. Nishimura, *J. Biochem. (Japan)* **46**, 219 (1959).
40. J. A. Gross and J. J. Wolken, *Science* **132**, 357 (1960).
41. R. Hill, *Nature* **174**, 501 (1954).
42. R. Hill, *Proc. 3rd Intern. Congr. Biochem., Brussels, 1955*, p. 225 (1958).
43. L. P. Vernon and M. D. Kamen, *Arch. Biochem. Biophys.* **51**, 122 (1954).
44. R. H. Nieman and B. Vennesland, *Science* **125**, 353 (1957).
45. H. J. Evans, *Plant Physiol.* **30**, 437 (1955).
46. D. E. Green, *in* "Subcellular Particles," Symposium Soc. Gen. Physiol. T. Hayashi, ed. p. 84 et seq.; Roland Press, New York, 1959; also Plenary lecture in ref. (19).
47. M. D. Kamen, *in* "Biological Structure and Function," Proc. 1st IUB/IUBS Intern. Symposium, Stockholm, 1960 (T. W. Goodwin and O. Lindberg, eds.), p. 277 et seq. Academic Press, New York, 1961.
48. D. I. Arnon, *Proc. 5th Natl. Congr. Biochem., Moscow, 1961*, Symposium VI, in press.
49. For a review, see B. Kok, general ref. II, p. 566 et seq.
50. J. Myers and C. S. French, *J. Gen. Physiol.* **43**, 723 (1960).
51. J. Franck, *Proc. Natl. Acad. Sci. U.S.* **44**, 941 (1958).

52. H. H. Strain, *Agr. Food Chem.* 2, 1222 (1959).
53. S. S. Brody and M. Brody, *Nature* 189, 547 (1961).
54. A. A. Krasnovsky and L. Kosobutskaja, *Doklady Akad. Sci. U.S.S.R.* 85, 177 (1952).
55. E. E. Jacobs and A. S. Holt, *J. Chem. Phys.* 20, 1326 (1952).
56. H. J. Trurnit and G. Colmano, *Biochim. et Biophys. Acta* 31, 434 (1959).
57. R. Emerson and C. M. Lewis, *Am. J. Botan.* 30, 165 (1943).
58. F. T. Haxo and L. R. Blinks, *J. Gen. Physiol.* 33, 389 (1950).
59. O. Warburg, G. Krippahl, and W. Schroeder, *Z. Naturforsch* 9b, 667 (1954).
60. O. Warburg, G. Krippahl, W. Schroeder, W. Buchholz, and E. Theel, *Z. Naturforsch*, 9b, 164, (1954).
61. J. B. Thomas and Govindjee, Symposium ref. [7], p. 475 et seq.
62. R. Emerson, *Ann. Rev. Plant Physiol.* 9, 1 (1958).
63. R. Emerson, R. V. Chalmers, C. Cederstrand, and M. Brody, *Science* 123, 673 (1956).
64. R. Emerson, R. V. Chalmers, and C. Cederstrand, *Proc. Natl. Acad. Sci. U.S.* 43, 133 (1957).
65. R. Emerson and E. Rabinowitch, *Plant Physiol.* 35, 477 (1960).
66. Govindjee, Doctoral Thesis, Univ. of Illinois, Urbana, Illinois, 1960.
67. Govindjee and E. Rabinowitch, *Biophys. J.* 1, No. 2, 73 (1960).
68. Govindjee, E. Rabinowitch, and J. B. Thomas, *Biophys. J.* 1, No. 2, 91 (1960).
69. W. L. Butler, K. H. Norris, H. W. Siegelman, and S. B. Hendricks, *Proc. Natl. Acad. Sci. U.S.* 45, 1703 (1959).
70. B. Kok, *Proc. 5th Intern. Congr. Biochem., Moscow, 1961* Symposium VI, in press; see also B. Kok and G. Hoch, *ibid.* Symposium VII, p. 397 et seq.
71. L. N. M. Duysens, symposium ref. [4], p. 10 et seq.
72. J. C. Goedheer, symposium ref. [4] p. 325 et seq.
73. M. D. Kamen, cf. symposium ref. [7], p. 483 et seq.
74. H. Leyon, *Svensk Kem. Tidskr.* 68, 70 (1956).
75. R. Sager, cf. symposium ref. [4], p. 101 et seq.
76. D. V. Wettstein, symposium ref. [4], p. 138 et seq.; also *J. Ultrastruct. Research* 3, 235 (1938); and *in* "Developmental Cytology," p. 123ff. Ronald Press, New York, 1959.
77. A. Frey-Wyssling, *Protoplasma* 28, 278 (1939).
78. J. J. Wolken, *Ann. Rev. Plant Physiol.* 10, 71 (1959).
79. J. B. Thomas, K. Minnaert, and P. F. Elbers, *Acta Botan. Neerl.* 5, 315 (1956).
79a. W. L. Butler, *Arch. Biochem. Biophys.* 92, 287 (1961).
80. E. Steinmann, *Exptl. Cell Research* 3, 367 (1952); see also E. Steinmann and F. S. Sjöstrand, *Exptl. Cell Research* 8, 15 (1955).

81. G. Brawerman and E. Chargaff, *Biochim. et Biophys. Acta* 31, 178 (1959).

82. G. Brawerman and E. Chargaff, *Biochim. et Biophys. Acta* 31, 164 (1959).

83. G. Brawerman and E. Chargaff, *Biochim. et Biophys. Acta* 31, 172 (1959).

84. H. Lyman, H. T. Epstein, and J. A. Schiff, *Biochim et Biophys. Acta* 50, 301 (1961).

85. J. A. Schiff, H. Lyman, and H. T. Epstein, *Biochim. et Biophys. Acta* 50, 310 (1961).

86. J. A. Schiff, H. Lyman, and H. T. Epstein, *Biochim. et Biophys. Acta* 51, 340 (1961).

87. H. T. Epstein and J. A. Schiff, *Exptl. Cell Research* 23, 623 (1961).

88. H. T. Epstein, E. Boy de la Tour, and J. A. Schiff, *Nature* 185, 825 (1960).

89. R. Y. Stanier, A. B. Pardee, and H. K. Schachman, *Nature* 169, 282 (1952)

90. H. K. Schachman, A. B. Pardee, and R. Y. Stanier, *Arch. Biochem. Biophys.* 38, 245 (1952).

91. A. W. Frenkel and D. D. Hickman, *J. Biophys. Biochem. Cytol.* 6, 285 (1959).

92. A. W. Frenkel and D. D. Hickman, *J. Biophys. Biochem. Cytol.* 6, 285 (1959).

93. J. W. Newton and G. A. Newton, *Arch. Biochem. Biophys.* 71, 250 (1957).

94. J. W. Newton, *Biochim. et Biophys. Acta* 42, 34 (1960).

95. J. B. Thomas, *Koninkl Ned. Akad. Wetenschap. Proc. Ser. C* 55, 207 (1952).

96. W. Niklowitz and G. Drews, *Arch. Mikrobiol.* 23, 123 (1955).

97. A. E. Vatter and R. S. Wolfe, *J. Bacteriol.* 75, 480 (1958).

98. E. M. Martin and R. K. Morton, *Biochem. J.* 64, 221 (1956).

99. J. A. Bergeron and R. C. Fuller, *in* "Macromolecular Complexes," Symposium No. VI, *Soc. Gen. Physiol. No. 6* (M. V. Edds, Jr., ed.), p. 179 et seq. Ronald Press, New York (1961).

100. H. Nakamura, C. T. Chow, and B. Vennesland, *J. Biol. Chem.* 234, 2202 (1959).

101. J. W. Newton and M. D. Kamen, *Biochim. et Biophys. Acta* 25, 462 (1957).

102. M. C. Karunairatnam, J. Spizizen, and H. Gest, *Biochim. et Biophys. Acta* 29, 649 (1958).

103. C. Bril, *Biochim. et Biophys. Acta* 29, 458 (1958).

104. J. W. Newton and L. Levine, *Arch. Biochem. Biophys.* 83, 456 (1959).

105. J. W. Newton, *Biochim. et Biophys. Acta* 42, 34 (1960).

106. J. A. Orlando, L. Levine, and M. D. Kamen, *Biochim. et Biophys. Acta* 46, 126 (1961).

107. See S. Aronoff, general ref. II, p. 246 et seq.

108. R. Y. Stanier and J. H. C. Smith, *Biochim. et Biophys. Acta* 41, 478 (1960).

109. R. Y. Stanier, cf. symposium ref. [5], p. 69 et seq.

110. A. S. Holt and H. V. Morley, *J. Am. Chem. Soc.* 82, 500 (1960); also cf. symposium ref. [5], p. 173 et seq.

111. T. W. Goodwin, general ref. II, p. 426 et seq.

112. T. W. Goodwin and D. G. Land, *Biochem. J.* 62, 553 (1956).

112a. R. C. Fuller, R. M. Smillie, N. Rigopoulos, and V. Yount, *Arch. Biochem. Biophys.* 95, 197 (1961).

113. H. Rudney, *J. Biol. Chem.* 236, 7, PC 39 (1961).

114. A. A. Benson and E. H. Strickland, *Biochim. et Biophys. Acta* 41, 328 (1960).

115. T. Horio and M. D. Kamen, *Biochim. et Biophys. Acta* 48, No. 2, 266 (1961).

115a. J. M. Olson, cf. symposium ref. [4], p. 316.

115b. S. Taniguchi and M. D. Kamen, *Biochim. et Biophys. Acta,* in press (1963).

116. R. G. Bartsch and M. D. Kamen, *J. Biol. Chem.* 235, 825 (1960).

117. R. G. Bartsch, M. L. Coval, and M. D. Kamen, *Biochim. et Biophys. Acta* 51, 2, 241 (1961).

118. M. L. Coval, T. Horio, and M. D. Kamen, *Biochim. et Biophys. Acta* 51, 2, 246 (1961).

119. S. Paleus and H. Tuppy, *Acta Chem. Scand.* 13, 641 (1959).

120. M. D. Kamen and L. P. Vernon, *Biochim. et Biophys. Acta* 17, 10 (1955).

121. J. A. Orlando and T. Horio, *Biochim. et Biophys. Acta* 50, 2, 367 (1961).

122. L. P. Vernon and M. D. Kamen, *J. Biol. Chem.* 211, 643 (1954).

123. R. G. Bartsch and M. D. Kamen, *J. Biol. Chem.* 230, 41 (1958).

123a. T. Horio and C. P. S. Taylor, quoted by B. Chance and M. Nishimura, *Proc. 5th Natl. Congr. Biochem., Moscow, 1961* Symposium VI, in press.

124. J. W. Newton and M. D. Kamen, unpublished observations.

125. M. D. Kamen and L. P. Vernon, *J. Biol. Chem.* 211, 663 (1954).

126. T. Horio and M. D. Kamen, *Biochim. et Biophys. Acta* 43, 382 (1960).

127. E. C. Wassink, E. Katz, and R. Dorrestein, *Enzymologia* 7, 113 (1939).

128. C. S. French, *J. Gen. Physiol.* 21, 71 (1937).

129. E. Katz and E. C. Wassink, *Enzymologia* 7, 97 (1939).

130. L. N. M. Duysens, *Nature* 168, 548 (1951).

131. A. A. Krasnovsky, K. K. Voinovskaja, and L. M. Kosobutskaja, *Compt. rend. acad. sci. U.S.S.R.* 85, 389 (1952); 92, 1201 (1953).

132. J. B. Thomas, J. DeGier, and C. Bril, *Biochim. et Biophys. Acta* 36, 326 (1959).

133. J. C. Goedheer, *Biochim. et Biophys. Acta* 27, 478 (1958); 38, 389 (1960).

134. J. C. Goedheer, Doctoral Thesis, Utrecht 1957.

135. E. Rabinowitch and J. Weiss, *Proc. Roy. Soc.* A162, 251 (1937).

136. See A. A. Krasnovskii, *Proc. 5th Natl. Congr. Biochem., Moscow, 1961* 6, in press.

137. J. C. Goedheer, *Nature* 176, 928 (1955).

138. J. M. Olson, private communication.

139. J. M. Olson, *Science* 135, 101 (1962).

140. J. W. Newton, *Biochim. et Biophys. Acta,* in press (1961).

141. J. M. Swan, *Nature* 180, 643 (1957).

142. J. F. Pechere, G. H. Dixon, R. H. Maybury, and H. Neurath, *J. Biol. Chem.* 233, 1364 (1958).

143. J. Lascelles, *Biochem. J.* 72, 508 (1959); see also G. Cohen-Bazire and R. Kunisawa, *Proc. Natl. Acad. Sci. U.S.* 46, 1543 (1960).

144. W. Menke, *Kolloid Z.* 85, 256 (1938).

145. A. J. Hodge, J. D. McLean, and F. V. Mercer, *J. Biophys. Biochem. Cytol.* 1, 605 (1955).

146. O. Wiener, *Abhandl. sächs. Ges. Wiss.* 33, 507 (1912).

147. W. Menke, *Biol. Zentr.* 63, 326 (1943).

148. R. A. Olson, W. L. Butler, and W. H. Jennings, *Biochim. et Biophys. Acta* 58, 144 (1960).

149. G. Weber, cf. symposium ref. [5], p. 395 et seq. (1960).

CHAPTER III

The Era of Radiation Physics: pt_s 15 to pt_s 9

I. Preliminaries

The primary data required for a reconstruction of events in this era are obtained from measurements of the spectroscopic properties of the photoactive components, *in vivo* and *in vitro*. The theoretical apparatus for the interpretation of such data is supplied by quantum mechanics. However, only very simple systems are amenable to rigorous treatment by quantum mechanical methods. By "very simple," one means something like a hydrogen molecule in the gaseous state, or a diatomic molecule which can be approximated for purposes of calculation by such model systems as linear harmonic oscillators, rotating tops, etc. Obviously, the complex systems presented by chloroplasts and chromatophores cannot be approached in such a fashion. Nonetheless, the fundamental concepts, established so thoroughly for very simple systems, can help as guides.

Initially it may be noted that in the very simple systems, emission spectra can be obtained by drastic procedures (high voltage arc and spark excitation, electrodeless discharge, etc.) which yield data in profusion for detailed correlations with model systems amenable to rigorous applications of quantum mechanics. If one uses as a model for a diatomic molecule a dipole oscillator which operates in a linear harmonic fashion (restoring force linearly proportional to separation of charge centers), and equates the bond distance with the average separation of charge centers located at the two nuclei when the molecule is in its most stable configura-

77

tion ("ground" or "unexcited" state), then one may visualize the total energy of such a system as in Fig. 11. This is a two-dimensional plot of the internal energy V as a function of the nuclear separation, r, and will be familiar to many

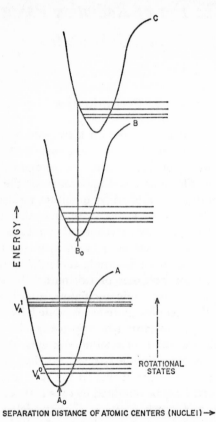

SEPARATION DISTANCE OF ATOMIC CENTERS (NUCLEI) →

FIG. 11. Energy diagram for a simple diatomic molecule (see text).

readers who remember their courses in molecular physics. Curve A represents the sum of potential and kinetic energies when the electronic configuration is that of the ground state and the nuclear separation varies. At point A_0, the nuclei are a bond distance from each other; they oscillate back and forth around this value of r with an amplitude indicated by the line $V_A{}^0$. At the absolute zero of temperature (0° K) all molecules are in this ground vibrational state. As the temperature is increased, some molecules take on increments of rotational energy until eventually they reach the next allowed vibrational state, $V_A{}^1$, in which they have a somewhat increased amplitude of vibration (shown by a slightly longer line for $V_A{}^1$). To anticipate a later discussion (p. 82), it may be stated that rotational energy increments are of magnitude 0.01 ev and vibrational energy increments of magnitude approximately 0.1 ev. For simple linear harmonic vibrators, these vibrational increments should be equal, i.e., $V_A{}^1 - V_A{}^0 = V_A{}^2 - V_A{}^1$, etc., but for real vibrators there will be a certain degree of anharmonicity which makes successive increments in vibrational energy progressively smaller. Continuing in this fashion, one finds increasing amplitudes of vibration in successive vibrational states, the envelope of which traces the curve A. Thus all vibrational and rotational modes of motion for the *electronically unexcited* diatomic molecule are represented by curve A. All excitations for curve A are assumed to arise solely from changes in nuclear motions. The form of this curve can be approximated analytically by the so-called "Morse function" (1).

There is a minimum in energy at A_0. To reach other points above A_0, energy is required. The points to the left of A_0 ($r <$ bond distance) show the rapid increase in V brought about by nuclear repulsion, those to the right ($r >$ bond distance) the somewhat less rapid increase in energy associated with the work required to break the chemical bond. Because the nuclei vibrate back and forth between the position limits set by the curve, they spend most of their time at the extremes of the position coordinates where their kinetic energy is minimal. Finally, if the vibrational energy becomes large enough, a point is reached on curve A ($r \to \infty$) where, in the portion to the right of A_0, the total energy becomes relatively constant and the nuclei can separate completely, i.e., dissociation occurs.

If the electronic configuration is changed by excitation

with a relatively large energy increment, ~ 1–5 ev, a whole new set of vibrational and rotational levels results. The envelope of these constitutes all the energy levels possible for the "first excited state," shown as curve B. Likewise, further excitation can give curve C which contains all the energy levels for the "second excited state." (Such rearrangement of electrons might involve charge localization, as in $H_2 \rightarrow H^+ H^-$.) The configurations allowed in excitation of electrons again are subject to limitations imposed by quantum restrictions which arise from the characteristics of the system involved. The energies required to achieve successive electronic excitations are so large that they usually are effected only by means of photon absorption in the visible and UV regions, whereas those for vibrational excitation can be reached by infrared absorption (heat absorption), and those for rotational excitation by absorption of quanta in the microwave region of the spectrum.

The stability of the molecular system in electronically excited states is much less than in the ground state, so that there is a rapid transition by various means back to the ground state. The transition, by emission of excitation energy as radiation (*fluorescence or phosphorescence*) is governed by a first order law, just as in radioactivity decay, i.e., the rate of change in the number of excited molecules in a given state is proportional to the number of excited molecules in that state at any instant. Half lives are of the order ~ 10^{-9} sec. The number of molecules in any of the excited states depends on temperature in a manner determined by the famous Boltzmann factor, exp $(-\Delta E/kT)$, where ΔE is the energy difference between excited and ground states, T is the absolute temperature, and k is the Boltzmann constant (1.38×10^{-16} erg/deg). The reader can convince himself by calculation that the number of molecules expected in the first excited state when $\Delta E \sim 0.1$ ev, e.g., for $V_A^1 - V_A^0$, and $T = 300°K$, is only a fraction of a percent of that in the ground state.

Next, one notes that transitions between the ground state and upper states are shown as vertical lines. This means the excitation process redistributes electrons much faster than the nuclei can move. The relatively great mass of the nuclei dictates this conclusion. In the ground state, transitions can occur to upper states anywhere along the coordinate axis covered by $V_A{}^0$. However, the upper states which should be favored for the new placement of the excited electrons will be those in which no new redistribution of nuclei is needed, i.e., those in which the major portion of the time of vibration is associated with the same value of nuclear separation as in the ground state. The kinetic energy of the vibrating nuclei is minimal or zero near the extremes of the amplitude range. Hence, the nuclei spend most of their time at the extremes of $V_B{}^1$, $V_B{}^2$, etc. A transition from the ground state (and back) will be favored, therefore, when the vertical line from the point of departure in the ground state intersects near an extreme of the upper vibrational level, as shown in Fig. 11. A second condition, which sharpens the transitions, i.e., minimizes the number of transitions expected, is that in the ground state there is no orbital angular momentum, whereas there are quantized increments of orbital angular momentum in the upper states. Hence, only transitions which involve the smallest time for partition of orbital momentum among vibrational nuclei are favored. All of these considerations are subsumed in the well-known "Franck-Condon principle," one statement of which is that *transition probabilities between states are greatest for those in which the change in internuclear separation is least.*

Now, to justify the rationalization of the time span during this era on the basis of the Franck-Condon principle, one notes that because vibration times, as deduced from frequencies of light absorbed, are $\sim 10^{-13}$ to $\sim 10^{-14}$ second, the transition time must be much less, i.e., $\leq 10^{-15}$ second. Hence, the shortest time is $pt_s \sim 15$. It must be emphasized here that in the case of polyatomic systems a simple diagram, as Fig. 11, is merely an oversimplified two-dimensional projection of an n-dimensional construction, so that the use of a vertical line to represent a transition may be misleading.

One might expect to see transitions represented by non-vertical lines. However, these considerations are sufficient to establish an order of magnitude for the extreme of pt_s at ~15.

Certain limitations are set by theoretical analysis of the simple case cited for transitions between the various vibrational and rotational states. Although these do not apply rigorously to most real diatomic molecules—certainly not to polyatomic molecules, and, least of all, to those contained in condensed systems—it is well to review briefly the quantitative relations which obtain for the various modes of nuclear motion, as based on consideration of simple systems.

Each electronic configuration is characterized by a total quantum number, N, or alternatively, by the electronic orbital quantum number, $L = (N - 1)$. In addition, each electronic state can possess two values of a quantized element of motion, called "spin," symbolized by the spin quantum number, S. Any transition is possible, given the requisite quantum energy in the exciting beam. However, "selection rules" for vibrational and rotational transitions dictate changes in integral quantum numbers (ΔV for vibrational, ΔJ for rotational) of ± 1. The rotational energy for a simple rotator is given by $(h^2/8\pi^2 I)\,(J + 1)$, where h is Planck's constant (6.6×10^{-27} erg. sec) and I is the moment of inertia. For $\Delta J = \pm 1$, the resultant calculated energy increment is only a few hundredths of an electron volt, as mentioned previously (p. 79).

A simple harmonic oscillator vibrates with a frequency $v = (1/2\ \pi)\,(k/\mu)^{1/2}$, where μ is the reduced mass [equal to $m_1 m_2/(m_1 + m_2)$] for nuclear masses m_1 and m_2, and k is a constant characteristic of the system. The quantized oscillator can possess this frequency of motion, which is identical with the zero point frequency (and associated energy) discussed above, or it can have higher values of vibrational energy given by the quantity, $hv\ (V + \tfrac{1}{2})$, where V is the vibrational quantum number. As mentioned previously (p. 79), the vibrational energy increment is of the order of 0.1 ev; the vibration amplitudes are of the order 0.1 Å. An anharmonic oscillator, which more nearly approximates the case for real molecules, can have ΔV values of ± 1, ± 2, ± 3, etc., the higher values being less probable. However, as the reader will remember, the ΔV values are determined by the details of the energy curves, such as those shown in Fig. 11, which result in transitions in accordance with the Franck-Condon principle.

The selection rules for absorption of energy by rotators or vibrators imply that only light which contains photons with energies equal to the differences in energy of the states involved will be effective in excitation. However, there is another important requirement. The exciting light photons have an oscillating electric field which must be in the same direction as the electric dipole moment of the molecule. Hence, a molecule with no dipole moment, such as gaseous hydrogen, will not interact strongly with infrared photons. Oscillators will absorb photons of the proper wavelength only if the photon electric vector has a component *parallel* to the direction of the molecular dipole moment. Molecular rotators require a component *perpendicular* to the molecular dipole.

All of this has importance for the particular processes of this era only if applied to the case of complex polyatomic molecules, like chlorophylls or proteins. However, the degree of complexity of the atomic motions which are possible for even the simplest polyatomic systems interdicts rigorous analysis in terms of simple harmonic motions. Still, it is often possible to express the molecular motions as a summation of harmonic motions, if a suitable set of coordinates can be found—the so-called "normal coordinates" (2). Any molecule with N atoms requires $3N$ coordinates to determine the location of all atoms. These $3N$ coordinates, or "degrees of freedom," include six associated with kinetic motion ("translation") and rotation. The remaining $3N - 6$ degrees of freedom are assigned to vibrations in the normal coordinate system, which must be constructed from appropriate linear combinations of the laboratory coordinates.

For a small protein with 2000 atoms, (6000 − 6) such combinations are needed! Obviously, theoretical analysis must fall back on approximations which consider groups of atoms acting as unit systems, rather than make constructions in terms of single atomic motions.

II. Some Asides on Absorption of Radiation

A. *The Fundamental Absorption Law*

Suppose that at a given wavelength, λ, the initial intensity of a collimated light beam is given by I_0, and that this beam exhibits intensity, I, after passage through a given amount of absorbing material. The *transmittancy*, T, is defined as the ratio I/I_0. In a solution layer of very small thickness, dx, the change in intensity, $-dI$, *associated only with absorption* (scattering and reflection losses are assumed to be minimal), can be deduced in the following manner. Assume each molecule presents a surface, σ, of dimensions such that any incident quantum is absorbed. The total effective area will be $\sigma\,Cdx$, where C is the number of molecules per unit volume, and dx is the thickness of the volume element. From the definition of σ, $-dI = \sigma CIdx$. Integration over a finite depth of absorbing solution, x, yields $I = I_0\exp(-\sigma Cx)$. If C is expressed in the usual way, concentration in moles per liter, and x in centimeters, then σ—termed the "cross section," or alternatively, the "molar extinction coefficient"—has the units liter/mole—cm. This follows from the requirement that the whole exponential term must be dimensionless. In decimal notation, $I = I_0(10^{-kCx})$. The cross sectional term, denoted by k, is called the *molar absorption coefficient*. More commonly, the unit concentration is given in millimoles per liter, so that k is presented as the "millimolar absorption coefficient," i.e., the cross section for one millimole of absorbent per liter or one micromole per milliliter. Magnitudes of k in liter/mole—cm for absorption bands of organic compounds in the UV and visible (energy equivalent quanta ~1–5 ev) usually are in the range 10^4–10^6. The "absolute" cross section, i.e., the cross section per molecule, or the molar extinction divided by Avogadro's number, is of the order 10^{-16}–10^{-18} cm^2/molecule. In practice, the quantity most often encountered is the "optical density" (OD), also known as the "absorbancy" (A), i.e., $A \equiv OD = -\log T = kCx$.

The equations shown which relate absorbancy to concentration, C, and path length, x, are a statement of the well-known "Lambert-Beer's law." They express the experimental fact that absorbancy is independent of light intensity, that is, the probability of absorption of a given quantum is not affected by any previous absorption act. This implies, of course, that no processes, photochemical or otherwise, intervene to alter the system permanently, physically or chemically.

The number of molecules in steady-state illumination in the ground state, A (Fig. 11), can be shown to be related to the number in the excited state, B, by the equation $n_B/n_A = I\sigma\tau/A$, where I is the incident intensity of radiation (number of incident quanta per cm^2 per second), σ is the molar extinction coefficient, A is Avogadro's number, and τ is the mean lifetime for de-excitation. It is easy to show that the ratio n_B/n_A will not be large even with intense excitation. Thus, for a light source which operates at 500 watts (a very strong source), and which irradiates an absorbing solution with light, about 5% of which may possess wavelengths in the visible absorption band of the absorbing molecules, $I \simeq 10^{20}$. A high absorbancy will correspond to $\sigma \simeq 10^6$/cm^2/mole. A reasonable value for τ (see p. 91) is 10^{-8} sec. Thus, $n_B/n_A \simeq 10^{-5}$, so that only a minute fraction of molecules in the ground state is raised to state B even by a strong light source. Because excitation events are so rare, they are unlikely to interfere with each other, so that absorbancy is essentially independent of light intensity.

It is possible to arrange conditions whereby this generalization is not valid. One way is to increase τ by excitation to a long-lived state. Another is to use extremely intense fluxes of light which can be obtained for very short periods of time. Both means are used in "flash photometry" (see p. 124) to study absorption characteristics of the so-called "triplet-state" level system, the ground level of which is the "triplet" configuration associated with the first excited singlet, i.e., the B triplet state in Fig. 11. (What is meant by "triplet" configuration is explained in Section D.)

B. Classical Bases for Absorption and Emission of Light

The harmonic oscillator draws energy from the exciting alternating electric field of the incident radiation only when the excitation frequency, v, matches that given by the energy difference in vibrational states, ΔE. The rate of energy uptake and radiation loss (emission) can be calculated precisely for the harmonic oscillator, but experiment shows that real atomic systems, however simple, require inclusion of a variable factor which is a measure of the efficiency with which the oscillator interacts with the exciting field. This factor is called the *oscillator strength* (f). When it has the value of unity, the system acts precisely like the expected classical oscillator. The oscillator strength for absorption (f_A) need not, and usually does not, have the same value as the oscillator strength for emission (f_B). If the system absorbs over a range of frequencies, Δv_A, and emits over a range of frequencies, Δv_B, then the quantities of interest are the *integrated oscillator strengths,* i.e.,

$$\bar{f}_A = \int_{\Delta v_A} f_A(v)dv \qquad \text{and} \qquad \bar{f}_B = \int_{\Delta v_B} f_B(v)dv.$$

The relation between f_A and k, the absorption coefficient, is

$$\bar{f}_A = (4.319 \times 10^{-9})n \int_{\Delta v_A} k(v)dv$$

where n is the index of refraction of the solvent medium surrounding the oscillator molecules. The experimental value of the oscillator strength for absorption can be obtained by graphical integration from a plot of k (v) vs. v over the frequency range of the absorption band. It can also be approximated by assuming a Gaussian distribution function for $k(v)$. In this case, the band width, ε, given by the difference in frequency at the absorption maximum, k_{max}, and at a point k_{max}/e, enters in the expression, viz., $\bar{f}_A = (4.319 \times 10^{-9})n\varepsilon\sqrt{\pi}k_{max}$.

The oscillator strength is the primary parameter in evaluation of the intensity of a given transition; it may or may not be simply proportional to k_{max}. In other words, the height of the absorption maximum is not a sufficient datum for evaluation of transition probability. In organic compounds, very high probabilities are associated with $\bar{f}_A$ values from 0.1 to 1.0 while low probabilities correspond to values less than 0.01.

C. Some Quantum Mechanical Considerations of the Briefest Sort

For comparison with theoretical expectations, the transition probability must be calculated by quantum mechanical methods. The oscillator strength, the notion of which comes wholly from the classical electromagnetic theory, can be related to a quantum mechanical parameter, the so-called "transition moment," M, which is a vector quantity derived from the interaction of the two electronic configurations involved in the transition with the electric dipole associated with the transition (3). The electronic configurations before and after absorption are described by wave functions $\psi 1$ and $\psi 2$, respectively. Transitions occur only if there are components of electronic configuration common to both wave functions. In practice, the calculations must be based on assumptions such as that deformations of the molecule caused by nuclear vibrations affect both states equally, or that many possible complex interactions in polyatomic systems can be neglected. When these assumptions are valid, selection rules which govern transitions dictate that only states of like symmetry can interact.

As the reader will infer, this restriction based on symmetry conservation is not strictly applicable in complex systems. Bands forbidden by simple symmetry considerations are often found, albeit with small f values (3, 4).

D. *The Matter of Spin*

Experience shows that in the building up of the periodic system, a generalization enunciated by W. Pauli and called the "Aufbauprinzip" ("construction principle") dictates the manner in which electrons fill the various atomic and molecular orbitals. This principle states that *no two electrons in a given atom can have the same set of values for all quantum numbers.* The quantum numbers are those mentioned previously, i.e., "principal," "orbital angular momentum," and "spin" (see p. 82). If the principal and orbital angular momentum numbers are fixed, as in a given orbital, then, if two electrons occupy it, they must have different "spin" quantum numbers. The spin quantum number is assigned the value $\frac{1}{2}$ and each electron in a molecule contributes $\frac{1}{2}$ to the total spin, either $+$ or $-$. If two electrons occupy the same orbital, their spins are $+\frac{1}{2}$ and $-\frac{1}{2}$, so that they are paired off and the resultant spin is zero. If all electrons in a molecule are so paired, then the orbital energy level cannot be shifted or resolved into components with differing energies by an external perturbation (e.g., an applied magnetic field), because there is no resultant electronic magnetic moment to interact with an external magnetic field. This type of energy level is called a "singlet"; a number of singlet states gives rise to a "singlet system." The reader may imagine curves A, B, C, etc., in Fig. 11 to correspond to these singlet states.

If there are two electrons in the molecule which have parallel spins, then the total spin possible is one, which may be oriented relative to an external magnetic field with component integral values of $+1$, 0, -1. Thus, because three new states differing in energy can arise in this fashion, the energy level involved for two unpaired electrons is called a "triplet." Again, there can be a series of triplet levels which comprise a "triplet system." In Fig. 11, curves A, B, C, etc.

will each have an associated curve for the triplet levels (not shown). In general, the number of levels into which a given level can be split in this way is called the "multiplicity," and is given by the expression $2S + 1$, where S is the total resultant molecular spin number (4).

The two possible orientations, $+$ or $-$, are designated by the symbols $\uparrow$ and $\downarrow$. The combination $\uparrow\downarrow$ will have spin zero, that with $\uparrow\uparrow$ will have spin one, etc. Most organic molecules have even numbers of electrons, all paired, so that $S = 0$ and the multiplicity is one (singlet state).

The total wave function of a molecule includes the product of functions for the orbital parameters (orbital function) and spin parameters (spin function). In general, transitions between states of different multiplicity imply transitions between states of different symmetry. This is strictly forbidden for sufficiently simple systems, i.e., ΔS must be zero for an allowed transition. However, just as in the case of removal of symmetry restrictions for orbital function by electric field perturbations or nuclear motions, so for spin functions there is a breakdown in the requirement $\Delta S = 0$ whenever molecules become complicated enough to have interaction between orbital and spin motion ("spin-orbit interaction"). The spin conservation requirement holds strictly only if spin can be considered wholly without regard to orbital motion. Furthermore, there can be violations of spin selection rules if the electron configuration involves components of electrical moment with orders higher than one, i.e., quadrupole, octapole, etc. The dipole transition moment may be zero, but there may still be finite values for the higher moments which allow transitions to occur.

"Forbidden" transitions, whatever their origin, are usually much weaker than those "allowed." However, as noted in the next section, there is an inverse relation between oscillator strength and half-life. Hence, "forbidden" transitions may be of importance in biology because by virtue of their low oscillator strength they may be very long-lived, thus permitting photochemistry to occur with greater probability.

E. Lifetimes of Excited States

Under special conditions, e.g., where absorption and emission bands are single, sharp, and coincide in frequency, it is possible to derive a relation between the integrated extinction coefficient (proportional to oscillator strength) and the rate constant, k_F, for emission (fluorescence). As verified in numerous experiments (5), fluorescence follows a first-order law, i.e., $dN_B/dt = k_F N_B$, where dn/dt is the rate of change of number of molecules, N_B, in the excited state B, so that k_F is simply a first-order rate constant. G. N. Lewis and M. Kasha (6) presented a relation in 1945 [see also an earlier treatment by R. Ladenburg 7)], viz.:

$$\int_{\Delta \nu_A} \sigma(\nu) d\nu = \frac{1}{8\pi c \bar{\nu}_A^2 n^2} \frac{g_U}{g_L} k_F$$

In this formula, $\bar{\nu}_A$ was the frequency at the absorption maximum, c the velocity of light, n the refractive index of the solvent, and g_U and g_L the multiplicities in the excited and ground states. These authors tested this equation by measuring the absorption spectrum of a dye, rhodamine B, in glycerol—a case in which the fluorescence quantum yield (defined as the ratio of quanta emitted to quanta absorbed) was close to unity (8). In other words, this organic molecule underwent no process of energy loss other than fluorescence so that the "natural" lifetime was identical with the "emissive" lifetime. The authors substituted for σ the molar absorption coefficient, k, and presented the relation in the form

$$\int_{\Delta \nu_A} k(\nu) d\nu = 3.47 \times 10^8 \frac{1}{\nu_A^2 n^2} \frac{g_U}{g_L} \frac{1}{\tau_0}$$

where the assumption was made, in accordance with the fluorescence yield close to unity (8). The value for $\int_{\Delta \nu_A} k(\nu) d\nu$, determined by integration of the experimental absorption curve, was 1.52×10^5, the frequency maximum was 18,050 cm^{-1}, the refractive index was taken as that for glycerol (1.47), and g_U was equal to g_L (because of spin conservation).

Hence, τ_0 could be calculated to be 3.2×10^{-9} sec. Experimentally, E. Gaviola (8) had found 4.2×10^{-9} sec. Thus, the theoretical relation was valid within a factor of two. In recent years more precise agreement between experiment and theory has been reported (5).

Another approach is to note that the observed lifetime, τ, is related to the emissive lifetime, τ_0, by the simple relation $\tau = q_F \tau_0$ (q_F, the fluorescence yield, is discussed in Section IV, D). In practice, the solution is irradiated, the absolute fluorescence yield is determined, and then the rate of decay is measured by a suitable fluorimeter after the exciting light is turned off. The rate of decay in fluorescence is too great to permit the use of simple mechanical shutters, such as are employed in "phosphoroscopes" (5), so electronic devices are employed. One device is the "Kerr cell," based on the "electro-optic effect," in which an appropriate liquid contained between electrode plates and subjected to an intense electric field takes on the properties of a doubly refracting medium, much like iceland spar. Thus, a beam of light can be passed through a Kerr cell situated between polarizing media such as crossed Nicol prisms, and thence through a system of mirrors and lenses to a second such combination. Very short time intervals between the passage of light from one Kerr cell to another can be arranged by a suitable choice of path length and spacing of voltage pulses on the two cells (5). Much of the early work on fluorescence half-lives was accomplished in this manner.

Modern researches have employed various phasing devices in which excitation is modulated at high frequency and the differences in phase between exciting light and fluorescence measured. An example is the work of E. A. Bailey and G. K. Rollefson (9) who measured τ_0 with precisions between 1 and 2×10^{-10} sec. These workers showed that τ for fluorescein solutions was $4.5 \pm 0.1 \times 10^{-9}$ sec. Most interesting from our viewpoint are the recent determinations, by O. D. Dimitrievsky, B. L. Ermolaev, and A. N. Terenin (10), and by S. S. Brody and E. Rabinowitch (11), of τ for chlorophyll *a* and other important photoactive pigments. The latter workers have used a special fast light source (spark) with an accessory oscilloscope device to follow the rapid decay of fluorescence. They have found τ for chlorophyll a in benzene, ethyl ether, and methanol to be, respectively, 7.8, 5.1, and 6.9×10^{-9} sec, with a claimed precision of $\pm 7\%$. In various algae, τ varied from 1.2 to 1.6×10^{-9} sec. Since the absolute quantum yield, q_F, for chlorophyll a in diethyl ether has been determined as 0.33, not only by F. Latimer, T. T. Bannister, and E. Rabinowitch using an integrating sphere (12), but also by G. Weber and F. W. J. Teale using a wholly independent procedure based on dipolar scattering (13), the emissive lifetime, τ_0, for chlorophyll a in diethyl ether is 15×10^{-9} sec. This value agrees with that calculated by use of theoretical relations [see, e.g., T. Förster (14)].

III. Electronic Spectra of Polyatomic Molecules

Figure 11 can be used qualitatively to deduce what may happen when polyatomic systems are excited by absorption of radiant energy. As long as the density of energy levels is small and differences in energy content are large, there will be a reasonably small number of absorption bands with relatively well-defined structure. Some overlap will occur in upper excited states, so that interactions will occur with consequent "radiationless" transitions to the lowest point of excitation, e.g., V_B^0. This process, called "internal conversion," becomes more and more probable as the number of levels increases and levels crowd together. In a polyatomic system, even with a relatively small number of atoms, this process is of major importance so that practically no emission takes place except from the lowest excited state. The fact that the lowest excited state is usually the sole origin of fluorescence indicates that there is little overlap between it and the ground state even in complex systems, while there is considerable overlap between the first excited state and other excited states. In $pt_s \sim 15$, transitions will be followed by rapid dissipation of excess energy via internal conversion processes.

It has been remarked (p. 88) that the levels shown in Fig. 11 correspond to the singlet system of electronic excitations, i.e., all excitations involve pairing of spins of the electron duo associated together in the ground state (assuming a system with even numbers of electrons as is the case in most organic molecules). If excitation occurs with unpairing of spins, the molecule will reach a triplet state from which it can arrive at the triplet configuration of curve B by internal conversion. The original triplet state could be reached by internal conversion from the corresponding singlet, or, alternatively, internal conversion could cause transition from an upper singlet to the lowest excited singlet and thence to the lowest excited triplet. This process is enhanced by close contact between molecules (as in chloroplasts or chromatophores) or by collisions between solvent molecules and excited molecules. The selection rules for emission at this point require conservation of spin, i.e., no triplet-singlet but rather triplet-triplet transition. The factors which govern triplet emission to the ground singlet are complex and not wholly understood, but experimentally they dictate characteristic values for τ (phosphorescence) $\sim 10^{-5}$ sec and longer, depending on experimental conditions. This matter will be treated later in the discussion of the triplet-state spectra of chlorophyll (p. 123).

The last complication one must mention is that in heteroatomic molecules there is the possibility of still another set of levels both for the singlet and for the triplet systems. Thus, when oxygen or nitrogen atoms are present in addition to carbon and hydrogen, transitions occur which involve interaction of wave functions associated with electronic redistribution to or from oxygen or nitrogen atoms. These transitions are called "$n-\pi$," as distinct from the "$\pi-\pi$" transitions which are associated with the singlet and triplet levels discussed hitherto (see next section).

IV. Molecular Spectroscopy of Porphyrins and Chlorophylls

A. Introduction

The drastic procedures for excitation of emission spectra of diatomic molecules are not applicable to polyatomic systems. Practically all data on structure and function of the photoactive pigments in the photosynthetic apparatus come from studies of absorption and fluorescence spectra. Thus, transitions observed are correlated with absorption by large blocks of atoms which may be treated as giant resonating structures. No detailed resolution is possible experimentally because the line structure in the bands is obliterated by molecular interactions. A typical *in vitro* absorption spectrum for chlorophyll *a* in diethyl ether (15), as an example of a photoactive pigment, is shown in Fig. 12. Two major band systems appear, one with absorption maximum at 429 mμ ($k = 121 \times 10^3$) and the other at 660 mμ ($k = 91.2 \times 10^3$). One asks: "What transitions correspond to these absorption bands, and how are they modified *in vivo?*" Definitive answers are not at hand. Hopefully, it will not be long before the happy day when the term level schemes for all the photoactive pigments, or even for just one of them *in vitro,* are in shape for textbook presentation. This hope is based on the extraordinary activity now characteristic of the whole field of molecular spectroscopy and quantum chemistry. While developments are too extensive to abstract in these pages, the reader can be directed to some of the literature from which he may deduce the status of research on the theoretical bases of porphyrin and chlorophyll spectra. Many of the ideas in this field as applied to biological function can be found discussed lucidly in the reviews of R. J. P. Williams (16–18).

Historically, E. Hückel introduced the molecular orbital treatment for organic systems in 1931. His treatment involved the assignment of cylindrically symmetrical "sigma" (σ) bonds for the single linkages of carbons in an aromatic, or unsaturated, molecule, and the use of so-called "pi" (π)

bonds with maximum electron density above and below the plane occupied by the σ bonds. Thus, in benzene, the σ bond system accounted for 24 electrons in twelve σ bonds, six formed by mixing atomic *s* and *p* orbitals of carbon and

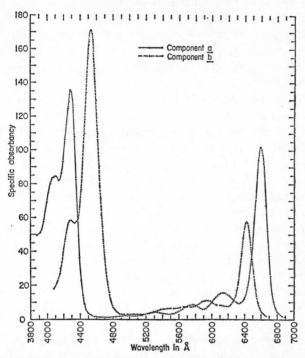

FIG. 12. Absorption spectra of chlorophylls *a* and *b*. After F. P. Zscheile and C. L. Comar (15). Ordinate: specific absorption coefficients × 10^{-3}; abscissa: wavelength (mμ). To obtain molar absorption coefficients, multiply by 902.5 for chlorophyll *a*, by 907.5 for chlorophyll *b*.

hydrogen and six by *s* and *p* orbital overlaps of carbon and carbon. The remaining six electrons were placed in three bonds derived from overlap of carbon *p* orbitals to form π orbitals. Shortly after Hückel's initial paper, F. Hund and R. S. Mulliken began their classical work on the molecular orbital treatment of diatomic molecules (19). Since then, the problem of porphyrins has been approached in the work of W. T. Simpson (20), who first introduced the idea of the

polyene model; H. C. Longuet-Higgins, C. W. Rector, and
J. R. Platt (21, 22), who pioneered molecular orbital treatments; and, most recently, M. Gouterman (23, 24), who has
introduced electronegativity as a single parameter to corre-
late effects of substitution in the basic porphin structure,
and who has also presented a treatment of triplet-triplet
absorption spectra.* The reader should also consult reviews by E. Rabinowitch (25) and by S. Granick and
H. Gilder (26), who discuss many relevant experimental
data.

All of these studies deal with transitions from one π orbital to another. However, the chlorophylls contain a metallic
central atom and certain important substituents such as the
carbonyl group, which make it necessary to consider transitions between metallic atom orbitals and the aromatic π
system, as well as transitions in which electrons move to and
from the oxygen and nitrogen atoms. These latter "$n–\pi$"
transitions have been discussed by J. R. Platt (22). The central idea is that the unshared electrons of the oxygen or
nitrogen atoms are available for excitation to the lowest
available π orbital. Such transitions often involve energy
differences of the same magnitude as the lowest energy $\pi–\pi$
transitions. They have been studied in some detail for formaldehyde, as the simplest case, by H. L. McMurry and
R. S. Mulliken (27).

M. Kasha has extended the analysis of spectra in terms of
$n–\pi$ transitions to a variety of compounds (28). The characterization of an absorption band as dependent of $n–\pi$ transitions requires the use of a number of criteria. One simple
test involves making the unshared electrons unavailable so
that no transition is possible, e.g., by protonation of the
donor atom in aldehydes, ketones, amines, phenols, etc.
Another criterion is the effect of different solvents on the
absorption maximum. Usually $n–\pi$ transitions require more

---

* B. Pullman, C. Spanjaard, and G. Berthier [*Proc. Natl. Acad. Sci.
U.S.* 46, 1011 (1960)] have described a molecular orbital treatment of
the iron-porphyrins, which is of interest in connection with the correlation between structure and function of heme proteins, see p. 34 *et seq.*
and p. 57 *et seq.*

energy as the polarity of the solvent is increased; this is in contrast to responses of $\pi-\pi$ transitions which usually show a shift of absorption maximum toward the red under the same conditions (28).

The developments cited above fall into two main categories—the strict molecular orbital approach, and a modified molecular orbital method which depends on liberal use of atomic orbitals in arriving at adequate recipes for wave mechanical formulations of energy levels. A third type of theoretical analysis is based on the approach introduced by H. A. Bethe and J. N. Van Vleck at about the same time Hückel was contributing his pioneer studies. Bethe and Van Vleck were concerned with rationalization of the spectra of compounds in which transition metal ions are surrounded by ionic or molecular aggregates, e.g., simple halides, hydration spheres, etc. They calculated energy levels for correlation with spectra based solely on expected electrostatic interactions between the central positively charged atom and the other groups treated as point charges. Covalent bonding was not considered. This approach in a modified form has been taken up vigorously and extended in recent years, in the form of the so-called "ligand field" theory of metal-complex compounds, by L. E. Orgel, J. S. Griffith, W. Moffitt, C. J. Ballhausen, and R. J. P. Williams, to mention a few notable contributors (29). Finally, there must be mentioned the classic researches of L. Pauling and his collaborators, which have supplied many brilliant insights into molecular structure, particularly of metal chelates, by exploiting the approach based on the use of single atomic orbitals—the so-called "valence bond" theory (30).

It is evident that there is a rich background of theoretical effort upon which to base speculations which seek to rationalize the observed spectra of photoactive pigments, as well as those of the auxiliary compounds which participate in the early phases of photosynthesis. The most recent suggestion for a working scheme in the case of chlorophyll *a*, *in vitro*, is shown in Fig. 13, as proposed by J. Franck, J. L. Rosenberg, and C. Weiss (31, 32). The data, on the basis of which the various transitions are drawn, come from

studies by P. S. Stensby and J. L. Rosenberg (33), and by
J. Fernandez, I. S. Singh, and R. S. Becker (34, 35). The
positions of the excitation levels in polar and nonpolar solvents are generalized from experiment and are not wholly
precise because the polarity of the solvents is not the only
factor effective. The exact nature of the solvent also has

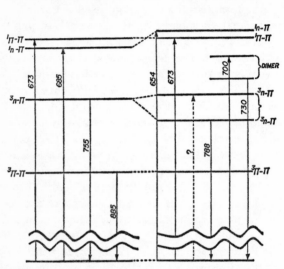

Fig. 13. Energy level scheme for *in vitro* chlorophyll *a*. After
J. Franck, J. L. Rosenberg, and C. Weiss (31, 32). (↑) Transition observed in absorption; (↓) transition observed in emission. Transitions
are indicated by wavelengths (mμ) of band maxima.

some bearing on where the absorption maxima occur. It is
seen that both π–π and n–π transitions for singlet and triplet
systems are included. The π–π transitions are those which
have been described as characteristic of conjugated aromatic
systems and which arise in the case of chlorophyll *a* from
the alternating single and double bond system of the tetrapyrrolic macrocyclic structure. The n–π transitions are
ascribed to the unshared electrons of the oxygen atoms
bonded to the keto carbon (carbon 9) on the cyclopentanone

ring (22). The authors emphasize that the relative positions of the first excited singlet $\pi-\pi$ and $n-\pi$ levels are reversed as polarity of solvents is changed. In nonpolar solvents, which are absolutely dry, $n-\pi$ lies below $\pi-\pi$, whereas in polar solvents, $\pi-\pi$ is the lower level. This deduction may be of fundamental importance in the interpretation of *in vivo* chlorophyll absorption spectra.

Some of the data required, not only to understand the spectroscopic characteristics of photoactive pigments *in vitro*, but to extrapolate such knowledge to possible conditions *in vivo*, can be derived from measurements of fluorescence parameters, studies on dichroism and birefringence, and polarization phenomena. These are surveyed briefly in the following sections.

B. Information from Measurements on Dichroism and Birefringence

There have been mentioned measurements of the dichroism displayed in chloroplasts (Chapter II, p. 66 *et seq.*). Interpretation of data obtained is based partially on *in vitro* measurements of the pure pigments oriented by various means. Thus, chlorophyll *a* can be oriented by adding to it, in solution, ammonium oleate which possesses both hydrophobic and hydrophilic groups. If this reagent is applied to a microscope slide and a concentrated solution of chlorophyll *a* in acetone is added dropwise, the whole being mixed and pressed down with a thin glass cover slip, birefringence develops in various areas of the resultant suspension (36). It is necessary to use an orienting substance which has no absorption bands in the visible range. Dichroism results because the chlorophyll molecules tend to concentrate in the layers formed by the oleate molecules, which orient themselves as banded or striped systems because the nonpolar ends draw together ("hydrophobic bonding") so that the polar carboxyl ends cluster in the water phase. At the interface, the chlorophylls concentrate with their nonpolar moieties directed into the nonpolar oleate phase. The porphyrin plates of the chlorophyll molecules are oriented between oleate molecules which are constrained into tubes. Polarized light transmitted down the axis of this tube will be absorbed preferentially by those chlorophyll molecules in which the major molecular oscillator vibrates in a direction parallel

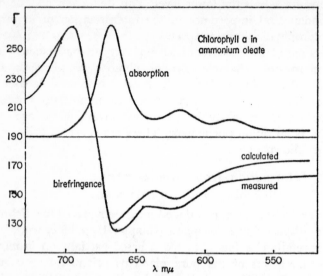

FIG. 14. Birefringence and absorption spectra of chlorophyll *a* in ammonium oleate. After J. C. Goedheer (39). The parameter plotted as ordinate is related to the birefringence [difference between indices of refraction for light with its electric vector parallel and perpendicular to the molecular plane, $(n_{||} - n_{\perp})$] by the relation

$$\Gamma = (n_{||} - n_{\perp})d$$

where d (in mμ) is the thickness of the refractive layer which contains the oriented chlorophyll. The birefringence contributed by the ammonium oleate is assumed to be constant over the spectral region shown. See ref. (39) for details.

to the electric vector of the polarized beam. Because the chlorophyll molecules can assume varying positions by rotation around the tube axis, the situation is not one easily amenable to analysis. However, Goedheer (36) has shown, with both chlorophyll *a* and bacteriochlorophyll oriented in this manner, that light which has its electric vector parallel to the plane of the porphyrin plates is absorbed preferentially.

A corollary to these observations is the expectation that birefringence—i.e., differences in refractive indices for light with electric vector parallel to, or perpendicular to, the optic axis of the molecules—will be evidenced by anomalous dispersion in the regions of wavelengths for maximal absorption. This phenomenon is closely related to the change in rotation of polarized light as a function of wavelength ("anomalous rotatory dispersion") which recently has become so powerful a tool for studies of protein structure (37). Goedheer's results for chlorophyll *a* oriented in ammonium oleate are shown in Fig. 14. Quite clearly, the expected correlation between anomalous dispersion and the location of the main absorption band is good.

The classical theory of Maxwell and Drude provides a basis for a calculation of the expected absorption coefficients in the region of the main absorption band (38). The quantity which appears in this treatment is the so-called "complex refractive index," the real part of which is the measured refractive index, the imaginary part the absorption coefficient. The measured dependence of the refractive index on the wavelength in the absorption band region gives the "anomalous dispersion" curve. At the wavelength absorption maximum, the refractive index goes through a minimum. Under conditions where the molecules are well-oriented and the transmission of light parallel to and perpendicular to the plane of vibration of the molecules is measured, the maximum value for birefringence (dispersion), denoted by Δn, can be calculated from the observed differences in absorption (ΔK) according to the relation,

$$\Delta n_{max} = \tfrac{1}{2} \Delta K_{max}.$$

C. Information from Measurements of Fluorescence Polarization

More incisive information on the vibration modes responsible for optical transitions in the various absorption bands of the chlorophyll molecules is derived from studies on the polarization of emitted light ("fluorescence polarization"). In these studies advantage is taken of the fact that linearly polarized (monochromatic) light preferentially excites those molecules in which the oscillators are oriented in the same direction as the plane of polarization. Goedheer (36, 39) has presented results of observations on the polarization of fluorescent radiation emitted from solutions of chlorophyll *a*, chlorophyll *b*, bacteriochlorophyll, the corresponding pheophytins, and phycocyanin.

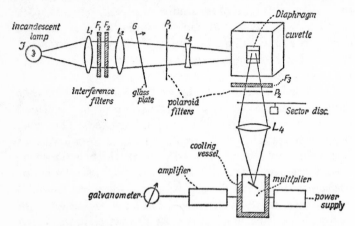

FIG. 15. Schematic presentation of polarifluorimeter (see text). After J. C. Goedheer (39).

The experimental setup is shown in Fig. 15. The exciting light, which originates at the incandescent lamp, I, is collimated and filtered through a system of lenses and interference filters ($L_1F_1F_2L_2$). Residual polarization is cancelled by the glass plate, G. The light then passes through a polaroid filter, P_1, where it is polarized, after which it is focused through L_3 onto the test solution. The fluorescent light emerges through a window at right angles to the direction of excitation. Scattered light is minimized by the filter, F_3. The polaroid element, P_2, analyzes the emergent fluorescent light, the intensity of which is measured for settings of P_1 and P_2 parallel to and perpendicular to each other. The sensing element is a liquid air-cooled a.c. photomultiplier tube used in combination with a rotating sector disk ("chopper") and an a.c. galvanometer.

Typical of the polarization spectra obtained are those for *R. rubrum* bacteriochlorophyll and the corresponding pheophytin (Fig. 16), wherein the absorption spectra are com-

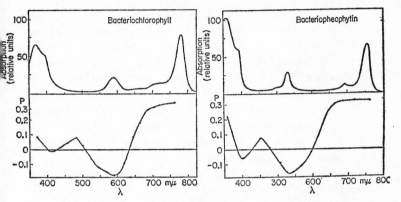

FIG. 16. Polarization and absorption spectra of bacteriochlorophyll and bacteriopheophytin, dissolved in cyclohexanol. After J. C. Goedheer (39).

pared with the polarization excitation spectra. The degree of polarization, p, at each wavelength, λ, of emitted fluorescence is defined as the ratio $(I_{max} - I_{min})/(I_{max} + I_{min})$, where I_{max} and I_{min} are the maximum and minimum transmissions measured for parallel and perpendicular settings of the polarized elements. F. Perrin (40) has shown that in solution, p varies between 0 and a maximum of $\frac{1}{2}$.

In Fig. 16, p, the degree of polarization, is compared with ε, the absorption coefficient, at different wavelengths for bacteriochlorophyll (10^{-5} M solution in cyclohexanol). The absorption maximum at 580 mμ exhibits a polarization of -0.18, which indicates that this absorption band is associated with an oscillator vibrating at an angle approximately perpendicular to the one responsible for the main absorption band at approximately 780 mμ. (A peak in the polarization spectrum at 490 mμ does not correspond to any absorption maximum; possibly a weak transition to a vibration band associated with the Soret region is involved.) Bacteriopheophytin has a similar set of correlations. The 580 $m\mu$ band of bacteriochlorophyll appears as a 530 $m\mu$ band in bacteriopheophytin, and the 780 $m\mu$ band is shifted to 760 $m\mu$.

In both sets of spectra, there appear to be two different oscillators operative in the Soret region which overlap in frequency. The expected degree of polarization for the combined contributions of two oscillators, perpendicular to each other and parallel and perpendicular to the oscillator responsible for fluorescence, can be calculated (41) from the measured absorption coefficients at 360 and 394 $m\mu$, assuming the maximum at 360 $m\mu$ is associated solely with one oscillator and that at 390 $m\mu$ with another. Goedheer finds in this way (39) that at 390 $m\mu$, 40% of the absorption is due to the parallel component, while at 360 $m\mu$ the same percentage is associated with the component perpendicular to the oscillator responsible for fluorescence.

One may pause here to note briefly how these results can be correlated with theoretical expectations, based on the suggestions of Longuet-Higgins (21) and of Platt (22), mentioned previously (see p. 96). These early attempts to rationalize porphyrin and chlorophyll spectra were based on the use of linear combinations of suitable atomic orbitals to fashion molecular orbitals. It was found that two types of orbitals could be derived which indicated increased electron densities for one type on the four pyrrole nitrogens and for the other on the pyrrole carbons in the position alpha to the pyrrole nitrogens. Transitions to an excited set of singlets and triplets involved movement of electrons to a peripheral position which was associated with an increased electron density on the methine bridge carbons. Such transitions had a preferred direction of oscillation dictated by the symmetry properties of the ground and excited states. There was a distinction between porphin systems which, because of their symmetrical conjugated set of alternating single and double bonds, exhibited a spherical symmetry, and tetrahydroporphin systems which exhibited cylindrical symmetry. The former were termed molecules with "round field spectra," the latter, molecules with "long field spectra." In round field spectra, transitions in one direction would yield the same energy difference as a transition in a perpendicular direction because of the spherical symmetry of the molecule. Thus, with porphins, calculations showed twofold degenerate transitions at approximately 690, 605, and 435 mμ; these values were in rough agreement with experiment. In long field spectra, transitions in two directions at right angles to each other were expected to have different energies because of the lower degree of symmetry in the molecule. In a case where the electronic transitions were sufficiently different in energy so that absorption bands could be separated and their polarizations determined, it was expected that a test of the calculations could be made. The following results of Goedheer for bacteriopheophytin are a good example of the correlations obtained.

Thus, from measurements of polarization of fluorescence and dichroism it was possible to determine transition directions (vectors) relative to that of the lowest energy. The absorption band for bacteriopheophytin at 765 mμ was found to be perpendicular in its transition moment vector to that at 530 mμ, just as predicted by Platt. Unfortunately, the actual energy differences were greater than those predicted by theory and the relative intensities of the two bands were not the same, as expected on the basis of this simplified approach. The more sophisticated approach developed recently by Gouterman (23), which is an elaboration of the earlier molecular orbital methods, appears to offer the hope that theoretical deduction and experimental measurements will achieve progressively better agreement in the near future.

D. *Observations and Deductions from Study of General Fluorescence Parameters*

More recently, Weber (42) has presented an elegant series of researches and theoretical deductions therefrom regarding the relation between various fluorescence parameters and the photosynthetic apparatus. This work may be abstracted briefly. The data collected bear not only on polarization of fluorescence, as noted in fluorescence excitation spectra, but also include measurements of absolute quantum yields for chlorophyll fluorescence, the fluorescence spectra of chlorophylls, the lifetime of the fluorescent state, and the degree of depolarization of fluorescence. As a background for an understanding of the significance of fluorescence yields, the reader can refer to the simple energy level diagram of Fig. 11, including higher-lying electronic singlet states D, E, F, etc., which he may imagine added to the figure. Excitations may occur because of absorption of quanta of such energy content that the various values of $h\nu$ correspond to the energy differences between A and the upper states B, C, D, E, etc.; fluorescence takes place only by emission from the lowest excited state B, because the molecule quickly loses excess energy by internal conversion (see p. 92). Hence, one may assume that only energy retained in state B can be used for photosynthesis. Energy can be lost from B by two processes other than that involving conversion to chemical free energy, as in photosynthesis with its characteristic rate, P. These are (*1*) radiationless transitions, which one may suppose proceed at a rate R, and (*2*) fluorescence, with the rate F. Process R is complex and not wholly understood, but for the present may be thought of as essentially a single process.

The absolute quantum yields may be defined for the three processes as: q_P (photosynthesis) $\equiv$ quanta converted in photosynthesis/quanta absorbed $= P/(P + R + F)$; q_F (fluorescence) $\equiv$ quanta emitted/quanta absorbed $= F/(P + R + F)$; q_R (radiationless loss) $\equiv$ quanta lost by radiationless transitions/quanta absorbed $= R/(P + R + F)$. Since R is not zero, there is no simple reciprocal relation between fluorescence and photosynthesis yields. However, suppose that the maximum fluorescence yield (for P = 0) is given as q_F^{max}, so that $q_F^{max} = F/(F + R)$; then $P/F = (1/q_F) - [1/q_F^{max}]$. [Note: the reader should check this result by substitution from the definitions given above.] Multiplying both sides of this equation by q_F, one finds $(P/F)q_F = q_P = 1 - [q_F/q_F^{max}]$. It is easy to see that an experimentally determined rise in fluorescence yield by a factor X will correspond to a photosynthesis yield of $(1 - 1/X)$. In some experiments, inhibition of photosynthesis has resulted in a five fold increase in fluorescence yield so that it is possible to have the very high value for q_P of 0.8. A complication is introduced, however, by the possibility, mentioned previously, that conversion in photosynthesis takes place from a lower-lying triplet state, to which the singlet state B decays by internal conversion. The factors which govern deactivation from the triplet state are not yet understood (see p. 128).

Thus, quenching of fluorescence results because of competition with radiationless transitions from singlet or triplet states, or because of competition with photosynthesis involving energy conversion from both kinds of excited states. As will be seen, there is much evidence that the value for q_P determined in the photosynthetic apparatus is an average overall the photoactive (chlorophyll) molecules, and masks the possibility that q_P varies from molecule to molecule, depending on the existence of varying structures (tautomers), states of aggregation, and "reactive centers" determined by neighboring nonphotoactive molecules. Thus, if there is a preponderance of chlorophylls with a low value for q_P in which are mixed a few molecules of chlorophyll with high q_P, the q_P as measured in the chloroplast becomes a measure of the efficiency of transfer of excitation energy absorbed by the majority of chlorophylls with low q_P to a few chlorophylls with high q_P.

G. Weber and F. J. W. Teale (43) have examined solutions of chlorophyll *a* and *b* and pheophytin *a* in hexane, both for the presence of tautomers and for verification of the basic assumption that q_F is independent of λ. They show that if tautomers are present, discrepancies will appear between the fraction of exciting light absorbed and q_F for various characteristic wavelengths. Their argument, with notations modified in accordance with usage in this chapter, follows.

Suppose a pure fluorescent compound is illuminated in solution with light of wavelength λ and initial intensity $I_0(\lambda)$, and that the measured intensity of fluorescent light is $I(\lambda)$. If $K(\lambda)$ is the fraction of exciting light absorbed, then $I(\lambda) = aq_F K(\lambda) I_0(\lambda)$ where a is a constant of the experimental system. For λ_{max}, the wavelength for maximal absorption in the band associated with the lowest transition energy, an identical expression holds. Eliminating a by division, and solving for $K(\lambda)$ in terms of $K(\lambda_{max})$, one finds

$$\left[\frac{I(\lambda) \cdot I_0(\lambda_{max}) q_F(\lambda_{max})}{I(\lambda_{max}) \cdot I_0(\lambda) q_F(\lambda)} \right] K(\lambda_{max}) = K(\lambda)$$

If the product of the quantity in brackets and $K(\lambda_{max})$ is plotted against λ, a fluorescence excitation spectrum is obtained which will be identical with a plot of $K(\lambda)$ against λ, provided the ratio of $q_F(\lambda_{max})/q_F(\lambda)$ is independent of λ, i.e., equal to unity.

Their experimental setup is presented schematically in Fig. 17. Continuous light from a hydrogen arc or tungsten filament, H, is focused on the slit of the grating monochromator, M, by a lens and mirror system, K. The monochromatic light passes through slit X into a light-tight box, B, which contains the cuvette, C, with its fluorescent solution. The detector, D, is at right angles to the direction of the excitation beam and filter, F, which absorbs the excitation beam and transmits the fluorescent beam. The resultant photocurrent is measured by the galvanometer, S, with its attached resistive load, L, electrometer, V, and pen recorder, R. P is the power pack for the detector photomultiplier tube, etc.

The results obtained are in complete accordance with expectation and prove not only that no tautomeric forms exist *in vitro*, but also that only one system for fluorescence is present in chlorophyll, and that q_F is independent of λ.

In vivo, τ for chlorophyll a fluorescence in *Chlorella* has been determined (11) as 1.6×10^{-9} sec. If all the chlorophylls have the same probability of emission at the moment of excitation, then from the relation $\tau = \tau_0 q_F$ and the measured q_F for *in vivo* fluorescence (12) of 0.025, one should expect $\tau = (15 \times 10^{-9})(0.025) = 0.3 \times 10^{-9}$ sec. The fact that the observed value of τ is five times greater (see p. 92) implies that the state of chlorophyll *a in vivo* differs from that *in vitro* in that there is heterogeneity in the emission sites.

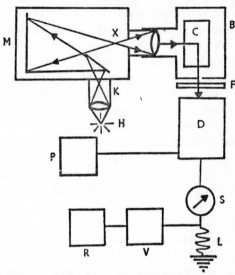

FIG. 17. Apparatus scheme for determination of fluorescence excitation spectra (see text). After G. Weber and F. J. W. Teale (43).

Heterogeneity can arise in two ways. One may suppose first that there are several types of chlorophyll *a*, with different values of q_F. A consequence of this assumption is the expectation that the various chlorophylls will have different absorption spectra. An *in vitro* model which may be cited is available from studies of fluorescence-quenching of flavins by complex formation (43). Riboflavin (RF) fluorescence is much more intense than that of flavin adenine dinucleotide (FAD) because of quenching by the adenine moiety. RF fluorescence, in the presence of free adenosine, is much like that of FAD. The mechanism involved is different from that which obtains in simple collisional deactivation, as when the quencher is an electrolyte like potassium iodide. In collisional deactivation the electronic excitation of the fluorescent molecule is dissipated as kinetic energy distributed between the emitter and the quencher. At low concentrations of the quencher, the efficiency of quenching is proportional to τ for the fluorescent molecule; as quenching occurs, τ decreases (40). On the other hand, the mechanism of quenching by complex formation, as with RF and adenosine, involves no change in τ. Weber (44) has found in this way that true complex formation occurs between RF and adenosine and that this is accompanied not only by a quenching of RF fluorescence but also by demonstrable changes in the absorption spectrum of RF. Thus, in the presence of adenosine (or, equally well, caffeine), the characteristic absorption maxima at 375 and 454 mμ diminish slightly and the long wavelength edge of the 454 mμ absorption band is displaced toward the red to a small extent. The changes noted are slight, however, and it is probable that such effects might be missed in the case of chlorophyll *a*, especially *in vivo*.

More recently, L. N. M. Duysens and G. H. M. Kronenberg (45) have shown that reduced diphosphopyridine nucleotide (DPNH) fluoresces in solution with a maximum intensity at approximately 462 mμ, whereas when it is in a bound form, the fluorescence maximum shifts toward the blue by nearly twenty mμ. As a model, they have examined possible complexing with the protein, alcohol dehydrogenase (ADH), and have found very similar phenomena. Not only is the shift toward the blue of the same magnitude, but the intensity of fluorescence is tripled. These experiments in complex formation between DPNH and yeast ADH parallel earlier observations on DPNH complexed with liver ADH, as noted by P. D. Boyer and H. Theorell (46). In more pertinent researches on chlorophyll, W. F. Watson (47) has noted that phenylhydrazine in small amounts quenches chlorophyll fluorescence without effecting any appreciable change in the absorption spectrum, a finding just like that of Weber for the effect of the removal of the nicotinamide nucleus from DPNH (48). One may note also that ethyl chlorophyllide and chlorophyll (phytyl chlorophyllide) show practically identical spectra [see A. S. Holt and E. E. Jacobs (49)].

An interesting example of the existence of complexes which are not identifiable by spectroscopic means has been cited by S. Ainsworth and E. Rabinowitch (50). These authors find that the photoreduction of the dye, thionine, by ferrous ions shows light saturation, a result quite unexpected for simple photochemical systems. A kinetic analysis leads to the postulation of a dye-Fe^{++} complex with a limited rate of formation in the dark. The action of light is supposed to be promotion of the complex to a metastable triplet state, catalyzed by the paramagnetic Fe^{++}, so that fluorescence is completely quenched.

The researches cited show quite clearly that complex and even chemically modified forms of chlorophyll may exist without any noticeable absorption characteristics different from those of monomer chlorophyll. On the other hand, as seen later in this chapter (p. 120), there can be marked changes which arise from changes in aggregation as well as from solvent effects (alluded to on p. 98, 133). It is probable that all of the phenomena prefigured in the discussion of crepuscular entities (Chapter II) can be attributed to such interactions.

However, it is more fruitful to focus attention on heterogeneities induced in the photoactive pigments which arise from the possibility of modification by *position* rather than by actual chemical change. Thus, one may suppose that some chlorophyll molecules are placed close to very efficient quenchers, while most of the others are arranged as close neighbors to each other in some semiordered system—layers, matrices, domains, etc. To obtain the experimental results quoted above ($q_F \ll 1$; $q_P \simeq 1$), it is required that practically every quantum absorbed find its way to a chlorophyll adjacent to a quencher. Light-saturation of photosynthesis results at such low intensities as to indicate that only a percent or less of all the chlorophylls present are sensitizers. Hence, one may equate the ratio of active chlorophylls at light-saturation of photosynthesis to the ratio obtained by comparison of chlorophylls adjacent to quenchers with the whole number of chlorophylls. This ratio, originally derived in connection with the so-called "photosynthetic unit" (51), is of the order 1×10^{-2} to 1×10^{-3}. It is obvious that heterogeneity, which gives rise to the discrepancy between measured chloroplast half-lives for chlorophyll fluorescence and those calculated on the basis of measured q_F and emission lifetimes of chlorophyll *in vitro,* can arise from "position" effects without noticeable spectroscopic shifts, because the active chlorophylls involved constitute so small a proportion of all the absorbing chlorophylls. Still another effect, that of modification of energy levels for chlorophyll by location in phases of different dielectric, may also be involved, as already mentioned (see p. 98).

At this point, one must consider the consequences to be expected from absorption of light by chlorophyll molecules embedded in a layered, or otherwise organized, system, whereby several hundred chlorophylls are near neighbors, e.g., as in a linear array. An excitation of one chlorophyll can be expected to be propagated to all of the others because of the existence of two kinds of mechanism; one is called "inductive resonance" or "weakly coupled" energy migration, the other, "exciton migration" or "strongly coupled" energy migration. Inductive resonance can be further distinguished as "homogeneous" or "heterogeneous." This terminology is not universal; it is to be hoped that there will be agreement in the future on a nomenclature for the various physical processes involved.

From the standpoint of the fluorescence studies, the process of immediate interest is inductive resonance energy migration (14, 52, 53), in which the probability that an excited dipole oscillator can transfer excitation to an adjacent one is a very critical function of the distance which separates them. In fact, if the probability of fluorescence (F) is equal to the probability of transfer (T) at a distance

(R_0), then at any distance (R), $T/F = R_0^6/R^6$. This relation, adapted to deal with the experimental data obtained for a variety of dyes in the presence of various quenchers, provides quantitative agreement between calculated and measured fluorescence yields and between calculated and measured ratios of quenched lifetimes to emissive lifetimes (43).

In addition, it is possible to establish that energy migration is taking place by examination of the degree to which polarized fluorescence induced in chlorophyll *in vivo* is depolarized. Thus, if excitation of a given chlorophyll in an organized aggregate is transferred successively to many others, the fluorescence finally emitted at the termination of migration will not "remember" in which direction the original oscillator was pointing, and so the result will be a loss of polarization relative to the initial polarized excitation. Weber (54) has derived a relation between p, the observed polarization after an average of n transfers, p_∞, the polarization observed with no transfers, and $\sin^2 \theta$, the average sine square of all the angles of orientation of oscillators which participate in the transfer, viz.:

$$\frac{1}{p} - \frac{1}{3} = \left(\frac{1}{p_\infty} - \frac{1}{3}\right)\left(1 + \frac{3}{2}\overline{\sin^2 \theta \cdot \bar{n}}\right)$$

For random orientation of oscillators, $\sin^2 \theta$ can be calculated and, as Weber has demonstrated (54), the average number of transfers, $\bar{n}$, which actually occur in solution of a given concentration, C, can be determined from a plot of $1/p$ vs. concentration; this is a linear relation at low concentration. In solutions of chlorophyll a in paraffin, an average value for R_0 is 36 Å. At high concentration, association of chlorophyll into dimers occurs and results in self-quenching so that the linear relation between $1/p$ and C no longer holds. The results of experiments on concentration-quenching of chlorophyll in solutions are completely in accord with the theoretical expectation based on the assumption that quenching occurs by transfer from monomer chlorophylls to associated nonfluorescent complexes, e.g., dimers.

The conclusion drawn upon extrapolation to layered systems, such as may occur in chloroplasts and chromatophores, is that many hundreds of transfers could take place before fluorescence occurs.

F. W. J. Teale (55) has examined the fluorescence excitation spectra and q_F values of chlorophyll a in solution in the presence and absence of a variety of quenchers, using an extended analysis based on the procedures outlined above. On the basis that the chlorophyll molecules are randomly oriented in solution, he derives a value of $\bar{n} \simeq 275$. Comparable values for chlorophyll in *Chlorella* are found, using as a quencher m-dinitrobenzene, which appears to penetrate chloroplasts readily and reversibly and does not produce detectable changes in spectroscopic properties of the chloroplasts. Teale concludes that the chlorophyll molecules are not oriented to any high degree because the calculated values for $\bar{n}$, found in solution assuming random orientation, are similar to those found in chloroplasts. He also concludes that, because fluorescence polarization of chlorophyll in organic solvents is unaltered by quenching, there can be formation of a weak complex between chlorophyll and quencher in the ground state which is not detectable as a change in absorption spectrum. This result is in accordance with those cited previously from the studies of Weber, Watson, Rabinowitch, and others (see p. 111). For direct evidence that nonradiative dissipative centers can exist in ordered organic systems, the reader should consult a later section (p. 138 *et seq.*) in this chapter.

Another argument is based on the characteristic times of events involved. Thus, the theoretical expectation (52, 53) is that the probability of transition is highest when the overlap between the absorption band for the unexcited oscillator and the emission band for the excited oscillator is large. This implies that in the case of chlorophylls, where overlap is essentially complete, the positions of nuclei in the excited state and ground state corresponding to the restrictions of the Franck-Condon principle are essentially fixed during interaction. This means that the interaction time, during which transfer must occur, is smaller than the vibration time of chlorophyll, i.e., 10^{-14} sec. If 1000 chlorophylls are involved and each transfer takes a maximum of 10^{-14} sec, then in 10^{-11} sec, all of these chlorophylls will have experienced an excitation. If the average time for fluorescence is no more than approximately 10^{-10} sec, a value determined experimentally (see p. 92), then an average of ten such excitations can have been experienced by *each* chlorophyll before emission loss of energy by fluorescence is required. Even if only one chlorophyll among these 1000 were attached to a quenching system, the chances would be good that excitation would be trapped in this chlorophyll. Moreover, the high degree of depolarization of fluorescence which is noted in chloroplasts would be a simple consequence of the multiple transfer process.

This simple argument needs modification in certain particulars. Thus, the Franck-Condon restrictions dictate that the excitation energy remain in the molecule long enough to allow the small adjustments in placement of atomic nuclei for maximal transition probability to occur. For instance, S. S. Brody has determined that there is a delay in the intermolecular transfer for energy absorbed by phycoerythrin and transmitted to chlorophyll *a* in the red alga, *Porphyridium* (56). When a light flash is absorbed by the phycoerythrin, he finds a delay of 5×10^{-10} sec between the flash and the onset of chlorophyll fluorescence. This effect, caused by relatively poor overlapping of absorption and emission losses, is not a complication in measurements of fluorescence lifetimes where chlorophyll is the only absorbing agent, however. Brody has also shown in a similar manner that energy absorbed by the protein in the chromophores of red algae experiences a delay in transmission to chlorophyll. From these measurements, he concludes that the chromophoric groups must be adjacent to each other, rather than separated by protein bridges; otherwise, it would be difficult to understand the observed high efficiencies of transfer between phycobilin and chlorophyll.

In any case, the observations on polarization and fluorescence yields are consistent with the notion that there is a rapid transfer of excitation received by any single chlorophyll in the chloroplast or chromatophore to a site where chlorophyll can sensitize a chemical reaction. Such migration is possible not only from singlet state to singlet state

$$\text{Chl}_{\uparrow}{}^{\downarrow} + \text{Chl}_{\uparrow\downarrow} \rightarrow \text{Chl}_{\uparrow\downarrow} + \text{Chl}_{\uparrow}{}^{\downarrow}$$

but also from triplet state to triplet state

$$\text{Chl}_{\uparrow}{}^{\uparrow} + \text{Chl}_{\uparrow\uparrow} \rightarrow \text{Chl}_{\uparrow\uparrow} + \text{Chl}_{\uparrow}{}^{\uparrow}$$

as shown by A. N. Terenin and V. Ermolaev (57).

E. More Remarks on Energy Migration, Photoconduction, and Associated Subjects

Heterogeneous inductive resonance processes have been well documented in the classic studies of L. N. M. Duysens (58) begun in the early 1950's. Prior to these researches, H. J. Dutton, W. M. Manning, and B. M. Duggar (59), and also E. C. Wassink and J. A. H Kersten (60), had observed that, in the diatom, *Nitschia*, the q_F for chlorophyll *a* fluorescence excited by light absorbed in fucoxanthol, an accessory pigment, was about equal to q_F measured with the exciting light absorbed by chlorophyll *a*. These results were readily interpreted as evidence that light absorbed by fucoxanthol became available for photosynthesis only after transfer to chlorophyll *a*. It might have been argued, however, that because of the low value for q_F (ca. 0.02), the photosynthetically active (nonfluorescent) chlorophyll was not necessarily involved in excitation by transfer from fucoxanthol. Duysens set out to examine the suggestion that the relation between action spectra of photosynthesis and chlorophyll fluorescence in *Nitschia* was accidental by determining action spectra for fluorescence in many other photosynthetic systems. In purple bacteria, as an example, he found in several species that the efficiences of carotenoids in inducing photosynthesis relative to that for the active bacteriochlorophyll (B890) were identical with the previously determined efficiencies for energy transfer from carotenoids to chlorophylls in diatoms.

One may also cite later experiments by J. C. Goedheer (61) who measured the action spectra for fluorescence excitation in suspensions of both intact bacteria and chromatophores obtained theref rom, e.g., in strains of *Rhodopseudomonas spheroides* and *Rhodospirillum rubrum*. The measured efficiency for transfer from carotenoids to bacteriochlorophyll in the former strain was 90%, in the latter 30%, and was the same in chromatophores as in the intact cells. Moreover, attempts to influence the efficiencies of transfer by addition of osmotic agents, like sugar and salt, had no effect, indicating no disruption of the geometric arrangement of the accessory pigments relative to the bacteriochlorophyll. Even extraction of much of the carotenoids from *R. rubrum* chromatophores by petroleum ether failed to affect the efficiency of transfer from the residual carotenoids, so that it appeared quite implausible that the low efficiency of transfer in *R. rubrum* could be explained by heterogeneity in the carotenoid system of the chromatophore. However, C. Bril (62) showed that treatment with detergents of chromatophores from another photosynthetic bacterium, *Chromatium,* interrupted transfer from the bacteriochlorophyll species B800 and B850 to the terminal photosynthetically active species B890.

It has been mentioned (see p. 41) that F. T. Haxo and L. R. Blinks had shown in 1951 that the chlorophyll *a* in red algae was less efficient in photosynthesis than the auxiliary phycobilins. This result seemed to indicate that energy absorbed by phycobilins could be used directly in photosynthesis. However, it was apparent that such a result could also be explained by the existence of "active" and "inactive" chlorophyll fractions. In fact, further developments led to the discovery by R. Emerson of the "two-quantum" effect (see p. 42, 171). The evidence now at hand from measurements of action spectra, fluorescence parameters, etc., is overwhelmingly in favor of the operation of both homogeneous and heterogeneous resonance transfer in chloroplasts and chromatophores.

As an alternative, there is strongly coupled or exciton energy migration, first examined theoretically by J. Frankel (63). This is a process in which the symmetry of the excited system allows its treatment as a single giant molecule or crystal. Because of strong coupling between neighboring molecules, the orbitals fuse into a single orbital extending through the whole crystal. Simply, the excited electron and the hole (positive charge it leaves) move together. The propagation time must be much faster than the lattice vibration times, so that exciton migration, when possible, is usually a faster process than resonance transfer. Among model systems in which it is observed are aggregated dye solutions (64). If the electron and hole do not move together, a charge separation occurs. This presents the possibility that differential migration, under the right circumstances, could set up electron-rich and electron-deficient regions wholly by a physical process without recourse to complex chemistry, and this could lead to a large q_P.

Experiments on dried chloroplasts have indicated that such intermolecular exciton processes can occur. Thus, W. Arnold and H. K. Sherwood (65) demonstrated that chlorophyll luminescence could be excited by heating chloroplasts previously illuminated at room temperature. Such a result would be expected if exciting electrons were trapped occasionally at imperfections in the assumed matrix or lattice structure and were released for later recombination with holes, upon absorption of relatively low-energy quanta in the infrared. Another consequence, photoconductivity—the migration of free photoelectrons under the influence of an external field—was also noted although not to the extent that one would unambiguously consider dried chloroplasts as semiconductors.

The notion that chloroplasts and chromatophores might be organized as semiconductors with a band system for electron and hole conduction appears first to have been enunciated by E. Katz (66). It has been elaborated extensively by D. R. Kearns and M. Calvin (67, 68), and also by A. N. Terenin and associates (68a). Kearns and Calvin have constructed model systems composed of electron donors and acceptors which are layered next to each other in a manner hoped to simulate conditions in chloroplasts. As an example, they have used phthalocyanine or violanthrene as donors, and chloranil, iodine, or tetracyanoethylene as acceptors. A thin layer of the donor is sublimed onto Aquadag electrodes on a glass plate. The electrodes are so arranged that the cathodes and anodes are closely alternate, like the prongs of two combs shoved together. A thin layer of the acceptor is deposited onto the donor layer. Upon application of a potential difference, a considerable dark current flows. Irradiation of the boundary between the layers by light which penetrates into the acceptor causes a small additional current (68). The quantum yield is estimated at close to unity. Some correlated data from measurements of induced electron spin resonances have also been presented (67). It is concluded that the photosynthetic apparatus contains donors and acceptors arranged in two-dimensional lamellae. Light energy absorbed by chlorophyll is assumed to migrate to the boundary where a charge transfer takes place between donor and acceptor, followed by charge separation via the intermolecular exciton mechanism.

A. N. Terenin and his associates (68a) have studied photoelectric effects in thin microcrystalline films of chlorophyll *a*, pheophytin *a*, and methyl chlorophyllide. They have shown that charge transport in such films occurs readily in the light and is carried by the "holes." The action spectrum for generation of this photovoltaic effect follows closely the absorption spectrum of the pigment.

The phenomena which are basic in the above studies and which relate to photoconductivity have been studied extensively in organic crystals and may be surveyed briefly. Conductivity based on photoionization—the movement of free electrons in conductivity bands—occurs in such systems as crystalline anthracene, naphthalene, etc., but only in small yields and if an impurity is present. Such a process is too inefficient to be useful in photosynthesis. However, higher efficiencies for photoconductivity can be obtained by insertion of metal electrodes into these crystalline systems. H. Kallmann and M. Pope (69) find from numerous observations that a greatly increased photoconductivity, caused by irradiation at the interface of crystalline anthracene and an anode, arises from injection of electrons from excited anthracene into the anode. Thereby, positive holes left in the anthracene diffuse to the cathode and are there discharged by electrons pulled out of the cathode. Apparently, the migration of the holes away from the anode is not impeded to any great extent. Furthermore, if an anthracene crystal is placed between two electrolytes and irradiated at one contact layer, there is a photocurrent which apparently is maintained by electrolysis of water (70). Again, the mechanism involves exciton migration to the surface from within the crystal, followed by transfer of electrons to cations in the electrolyte and subsequent migration of the positive holes in the crystal to the dark boundary, where there is a reduction of anions in the electrolyte bathing the dark surface of the crystal. These experiments are performed with specially constructed cells that permit working with very thin single crystals (ca. 10 μ thick). Because of the minute currents generated (ca. 10^{-9} amp), it is quite impracticable to isolate the gaseous hydrogen and oxygen expected from water electrolysis, but there seems to be no reasonable alternative to the supposition that water electrolysis is the process involved.

F. Dimeric Chlorophyll

A. A. Krasnovsky and his collaborators (71, 72), as well as S. S. and M. Brody (73, 74), and J. Lavorel (75) have proposed the existence of chlorophyll in aggregated forms, both *in vitro* and *in vivo*. Concentrated solutions of chlorophyll show a quenching of fluorescence (75, 76) which can be attributed to self-quenching by dimers of chlorophyll.

As discussed previously (see p. 113), the idea of transfer

of excitation through a chain of monomers to a dimer has been employed by G. Weber (42) to explain quantitatively this type of concentration-quenching. He derives a relation between K, the dimer dissociation constant, and the ratio of quantum yields of fluorescence in the presence and absence of quencher as the concentration of chlorophyll is varied. Independent determinations of the number of transfers from measurements of concentration depolarization of fluorescence (see p. 113) leave only K and the relative quantum yields as parameters. The curve obtained, assuming $K = 0.22$ M, agrees within a few percent with the experimental findings of W. F. Watson and R. L. Livingston (77) for chlorophyll a in ether solution. The major conclusion from these data, if they are applicable to chlorophyll in chloroplasts, is that there is a much smaller proportion of dimers present in chloroplasts than one would expect from the relatively enormous concentrations calculated on the basis of any model in which the chlorophylls are localized in layered arrays.

Others adopt an opposed view. S. S. Brody (73) has found a sharp fluorescence band at 720 mμ in *Chlorella* and *Porphyridium* species when these organisms are cooled to liquid air temperatures ($-193°$ C). He assumes that this fluorescence band, previously unknown, arises from the same source as a 715 mμ fluorescence emitted from concentrated ethanolic solutions of chlorophyll a at these low temperatures. (Direct evidence for the existence of aggregates has been given by F. Rodrigo (78) who finds the average molecular weight of chlorophyll to be nearly three times normal in 10^{-3} M acetone solutions of chlorophyll a.) No such fluorescence is found in crystalline preparations of chlorophylls or corresponding chlorophyllides, prepared as described by A. S. Holt and E. E. Jacobs (49). In *Porphyridium*, there is the possibility that the new fluorescence could be ascribed to a form of chlorophyll, labeled "d," the existence of which had been proposed by L. N. M. Duysens (58) to explain a low yield of chlorophyll a-sensitized photosynthesis excited in the long wavelength side of the 660 mμ chlorophyll band. Duysens, as well as S. French and V. K. Young (79), have reported the 720 mμ fluorescence in *Porphyridium*.

Recently, W. L. Butler (80), working with the same phenomenon—namely, the new fluorescence band at 720 mμ which appears at low temperatures—associates this fluorescence with a 705 mμ absorbing form of chlorophyll. He regards dimerization of such chlorophyll, bound as a small fraction of the chlorophyll in the lamellar lipoprotein, as unlikely, and suggests instead a chlorophyll-cytochrome adduct both as the source of the fluorescence and as the energy trap for radiation absorbed in the chloroplast and utilized in photosynthesis—a suggestion favored by a number of other workers (see p. 142).

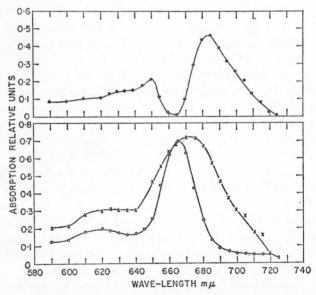

FIG. 18. Absorption spectra of chlorophyll *a* in ethanol. After S. S. and M. Brody (74). The two lower curves show absorption of 10^{-5} M (—o—o—) and 3×10^{-2} M (—x—x—) solutions. A difference spectrum for these two curves is exhibited above and reveals maxima at 682 and 648 mμ, which are assumed to be associated with the dimeric form of chlorophyll *a*.

Brody has shown that alcoholic extracts from *Porphyridium* show no 720 mμ fluorescence (73). The absorption spectrum of the dimer derived by the Brodys (74) from difference spectra of 3×10^{-2} M and 1×10^{-5} M chlorophyll solutions in ethanol is shown in Fig. 18. More recently, M. Brody and H. Linschitz (80a) have determined fluorescence spectra, at room and liquid air temperatures, for various algae, leaves of higher plants, and some photosynthetic bacteria. Using the enhancement of the long wavelength fluorescence at low temperatures as a criterion, they find very large amounts of the aggregated chlorophyll *a* in *Euglena* and in *Porphyridium*. Other green organisms examined show varying amounts of the aggregated component; however, there appears to be no evidence for more than one form of fluorescent bacteriochlorophyll in bacteria. The coexistence of two forms of fluorescent chlorophyll—the monomeric and the aggregated (dimeric) forms—in the green plant and algae systems, and of only one in the bacteria is very suggestive, in view of the apparent absence of Emerson's quantum-cooperation effect in the bacteria (see p. 63), as well as the absence of an oxygen-evolving system in bacterial photosyntheses. It would appear that aggregation phenomena can be evoked to account for many of the crepuscular components of the photosynthetic apparatus.

G. *Triplet-State Chlorophyll*

The obvious advantages of a relatively long-lived excited state of chlorophyll for energy storage and conversion has inspired much research and speculation. The limitation at $pt_s \sim 9$ for the photophysical era is based on the longest allowed times for decay of singlet-singlet fluorescence. As mentioned previously (see p. 5, 93), conversion of the lowest-lying excited singlet to a lower-lying triplet would give rise to a metastable phosphorescent state which might be longer-lived than the first excited singlet by many orders of magnitude. The existence of such an excited state and its associated higher triplet levels has been inferred indirectly from a variety of studies on fluorescence-quenching, bleaching of chlorophyll in steady-state photosynthesis, and data on the kinetics of sensitization (81, 82). Demonstrations of its existence have been obtained by means of flash spectrophotometry. Thus, R. L. Livingston and his co-workers (83) have presented data on the absorption spectra and lifetimes associated with the metastable state, as have H. Linschitz and his collaborators (84, 85).

The method of flash spectrophotometry, developed by G. Porter (86) for the study of free-radical reactions depends on the fact that most, if not all, the molecules of any compound in solution can be raised to an excited state by a short pulse of very intense light, provided the mean lifetime of the excited state is comparable to, or longer than, the flash time. Suppose, as in Fig. 11, that chlorophyll molecules in ground state A are excited to states B, C, etc., by a flash which lasts approximately 10^{-6} sec. All of the excited molecules will decay by internal conversion to state B, the lowest excited singlet, in a negligible time compared to the natural emissive lifetime ($\tau \ll 10^{-9}$ sec). From B, there will be a finite probability that an appreciable percentage will be transformed to the associated triplet B state which should lie at a lower energy level by Hund's rule.[1] The molecules trapped in triplet state B will remain there for the long time required by the forbidden nature of the triplet B-singlet A transition, say approximately 10^{-5} to 10^{-4} sec. Meanwhile, most of the molecules which did not leave singlet B will have decayed to the ground state in the usual fluorescence process in approximately 10^{-8} sec. However, because the flash lasts one hundred times longer than this, the process of excitation is repeated one hundred times and so the end result is the trapping in the B triplet state of all the molecules originally excited to the singlet states. Experimentally, the trick is to get intense flashes which have a "profile"—time variation—with a very fast rise time and a

---

[1] A principle derived from experience with atomic spectra which states that of various term levels given by equivalent electrons those with greatest multiplicity lie deepest (have lowest energy).

negligible "tail," so that the flash itself does not interfere with the examination of the actual absorbancy change brought about by the relocation of all ground-state singlet molecules in the new "ground" triplet state. The other features of the experimental setup involve triggering mechanisms for synchronizing the flash with the shutter which activates the analyzing light and electronic gear for studying the rapid absorbancy changes.

One may cite recent experiments by H. Linschitz and K. Sarkanen (85). A block diagram of the apparatus is shown in Fig. 19. The general procedure is as follows: The light

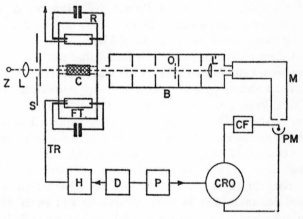

Fig. 19. Flash spectrophotometer apparatus (see text). After H. Linschitz and K. Sarkanen (85).

from the d.c. arc source (Z), collimated by the lens system (L,L') and baffle (B), is passed through the test cuvette (C) and a wavelength selected from the emergent beam by the monochromator M). The intensity transmitted is measured by a photomultiplier tube (PM) connected through the cathode follower (CF) to the oscillograph (CRO). By means of the pulsing circuit, comprised of the high-voltage firing-pulse generator (H), a time-pulse generator (P), and a suitable delay circuit (D), the oscilloscope sweep is triggered, and then all the flash tubes are fired together. Reflectors

(R) are mounted to collect all the exciting light possible. Sweep and flashes are recorded with the shutter (S) open and closed. The trace of absorbancy change with time with the shutter closed gives a horizontal base line for reference, and changes in the vertical dimension with the shutter open and closed give the absorbancy change owing to the presence of the metastable state. This absorbancy change added to that for the ground-state molecules, as determined in the usual manner, gives the absorbancy of the excited molecules. The rate of decay is also followed. These measurements are repeated at appropriate wavelength intervals determined by intensities transmitted for reasonably small slit openings. For example, at 480 mμ, full-scale deflections which correspond to transmissions between 0–5% can be obtained with a monochromator slit width of 4 mμ.

In these measurements it was found that the same decay rates were exhibited at all exciting wavelengths so that the spectrum obtained could be assumed with some certainty to be that from a single level in the triplet system, namely, that corresponding to the lowest-lying triplet. The total heating of the solution was negligible, and the chlorophyll recovered after numerous trials appeared unchanged, as tested by spectroscopic examination. Extreme care was exercised in degassing and drying the solvent systems to avoid decomposition by traces of oxygen and water which could have caused irreversible photooxidation and degradation of the reactive metastable chlorophyll. The absorption spectrum, determined in this fashion, for excited chlorophyll *a* in pyridine is shown in Fig. 20, together with the absorption spectrum for unexcited chlorophyll.

No one looking at this spectrum would recognize a fused tetrapyrrolic structure as associated with it. More likely, one would think of a bile pigment. Indeed, one could suppose that the loss of the Soret band might be attributed to a break in the resonating macrocyclic system of the basic dihydroporphin structure. Because this break is reversible in the absence of oxygen and water, it is likely that the chemical nature of the metastable state is attributable to a partial oxidation (or reduction) at the bridge carbons or at the nitrogen-carbon linkages of the pyrrole rings. Linschitz and Sarkanen note that the metastable-state spectra are reminiscent of those found for the intermediates of the phase test (87). They also look like the spectra of the intermediates

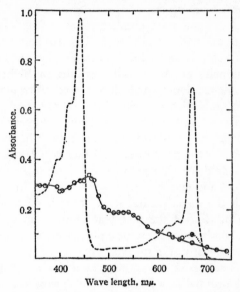

Fig. 20. Absorption spectra of chlorophyll *a* and its metastable state in pyridine, 2.1×10^{-6} *M*. Ground state (- - -); metastable state (———). After H. Linschitz and K. Sarkanen (85).

in the famous reversible photoreduction reactions discovered by A. A. Krasnovsky and his collaborators (see Chapter IV). The extremely broad maxima indicate considerable overlapping of electronic states.

Theoretical analysis is as yet in a preliminary stage. M. Gouterman (24) has published a theory for the triplet excited states of porphins in which he considers the case for a metalloporphin, zinc tetraphenylporphin. The model employed is that of bound electrons in a "circular box" which give rise to electronic states to which characteristic total angular momentum numbers can be assigned. For the ground state of porphin, the pair of highest-filled orbitals —those with orbital angular momentum numbers equal to four—are filled with four electrons. This state is denoted $(4)^4$, and its resultant total angular momentum along a predetermined Z axis is zero. The first excited configuration is obtained by raising one of these electrons into an orbital with angular momentum number equal to five. The resultant configuration is denoted $(4)^3 5$. This configuration gives rise to both singlet and triplet states. Further triplet-triplet transitions arise either from transitions to higher singly excited configurations or to a doubly excited configuration, i.e., $(4)^2(5)^2$, in which two electrons and two positive holes are left in the orbital pairs with angular momentum number equal to four, and two electrons appear in the orbital pairs with angular momentum number equal to five. This doubly excited configuration gives computed transition probabilities and energy increments which are in fair agreement with the experimental data. This is particularly remarkable in view of the fact that there is no satisfactory theoretical basis for computation of effects due to the heteroatoms (nitrogens) in the porphin ring.

Kinetic analyses of the absorbancy time changes for flash-excited chlorophylls (78) and for porphyrins and aromatic hydrocarbons (88) show that the triplet reversion to the singlet ground state is very complex. The rate law is

$$-dC^*/dt = k_1 C^* + k_2 (C^*)^2 + k_3 (C^*)(C_g) + k_4 (C^*)(M)$$

where C^* and C_g are concentrations of triplet- and ground-state molecules, respectively, and M is the concentration of a quenching agent. Thus, one sees that the decay law is not a simple first-order process dependent only on the instantaneous concentration of triplet-state molecules. For chlorophyll a in pyridine, Linschitz and Sarkanen give $k_1 = 670$ sec^{-1}, $k_2 = 1.5 \times 10^{-9}$ liter mole^{-1} sec^{-1}, and $k_3 = 2 \times 10^7$ liter mole^{-1} sec^{-1}. The significance of k_1 and k_2 is obvious, but that of k_3 is not. It is difficult to imagine the physical basis for an interaction between ground state and triplet state, but the values for k_3 show that this interaction is not negligible.

The quenching constant, k_4, depends on the nature of the excited molecule and the quencher and has been evaluated for a variety of systems by H. Linschitz and L. Pekkarinen (88). For triplet-state anthracene and porphyrins dissolved in pyridine and tetrahydrofuran, paramagnetic transition metals show values for k_4 in the vicinity of 10^8 liter mole^{-1} sec^{-1}, but k_4 for Mn^{++} is abnormally low (approximately 10^6), and some strongly paramagnetic rare earth ions have very small constants (less than 5×10^5). These results are quite surprising, because one might anticipate that strongly paramagnetic ions would all be strong quenchers, by virtue of their high resultant electronic spin moments which should lead to strong spin-orbit interactions in the excited molecules arising from the inhomogeneous

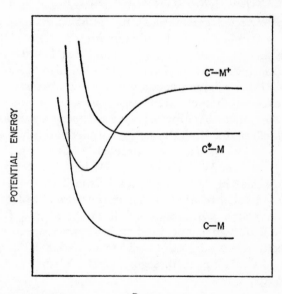

FIG. 21. Energy relations suggested for interaction between substrate (C) and quencher (M) molecules (see text). After H. Linschitz and L. Pekkarinen (88).

field produced by the high-spin quenching ion. Moreover, it is known that the presence of water strongly diminishes triplet-state quenching by transition metal ions, although no appreciable change in magnetic moment of the quencher is involved. The conclusion is reached (88) that a chemical rather than a physical mechanism is involved, at least in some cases. A plausible hypothesis is that of a "charge transfer" mechanism, as shown in Fig. 21 in which a ground-state complex, denoted "C-M," leads to the excited complex "C*-M." The potential energy curves for C*-M crosses that for a product system C^--M^+ obtained by transfer of charge from M to C* with consequent deactivation of C*. As discussed later (Chapter IV), this mechanism is very possibly of general importance in the primary chemistry of the photochemical era.

H. Electron Spin Resonance (ESR)

The expected paramagnetic nature of triplet-state molecules was indicated in the pioneer investigations of G. N. Lewis and M. Calvin (89), who found that fluorescein dissolved in boric acid and irradiated with a high flux of blue light, so that a large fraction of the dye molecules reached the excited phosphorescent state, became paramagnetic. However, demonstration of expected paramagnetic resonance effects for optically excited triplet-state phosphorescent molecules was lacking until recently when C. A. Hutchison, Jr. and B. W. Mangum (90, 91) found a strong resonance signal in deuterated naphthalene dissolved in deuterated durene, relative to that in the normal system (91). B. Commoner, J. J. Heise, and J. Townsend (92) first reported ESR signals associated with illumination of photosynthetic systems in 1954; their reports were followed by those of G. Tollin, P. B. Sogo, and M. Calvin (93) shortly thereafter.

In brief, suspensions of algae usually show a light-dependent signal associated with magnetic resonance frequencies characteristic of an essentially free electron. M. B. Allen, L. H. Piette, and J. C. Murchio (94) have determined an action spectrum for the light production of the free-electron signal which decays rapidly when the lights are turned off; these authors show participation of both C_a695 and C_a710, a result also reported by Calvin's group (95). It is evident that the application of ESR methods to photosynthetic systems may well be a very active field, and so a little of our precious space should be given to a discussion of what may be hoped for in future developments.

First, let us review the basic principles of the method (95). I have mentioned (see p. 88) that the spin parameter of the electron enables it to assume orientations which are quantized in spin angular momentum relative to an applied strong external magnetic field. The various levels into which the original orbital of the atom containing unpaired electron spins is split differ by an energy $E = g\beta H$, where β is a fundamental unit called the "Bohr magneton," dependent wholly on fundamental constants; H is the applied field at the atomic dipole; and g is a constant characteristic of the coupling between the electron spin moment and the external field. The constant, g, includes as a factor the inherent magnetic moment of the electron and, for a free electron, has the value 2.0023. This value is obtained by observing a "resonance frequency" $v = \Delta E/h = g\beta H/h$. This resonance is strictly a quantum mechanical effect and arises in the following manner. At equilibrium in a given field, H, there will be more atoms in the lower-lying pair of the two states which result by interaction of spin $\frac{1}{2}$ to give total orbital momenta, $L + \frac{1}{2}$ and $L - \frac{1}{2}$, as projected on the axis of the applied field. While the difference in population of states, given by the Boltzmann factor, $\exp(-\Delta E/kT)$, is very small, a change in this difference is readily ascertained. If an energy equivalent in frequency to the natural frequency, v, associated with E, is fed into the system, there will be an interaction (resonance) in which this energy is absorbed and some atoms "flipped" in spin, so that they move from the lower state to the upper state. The frequencies involved are in the microwave range. The loss of energy from the excitation beam can be seen by keeping constant the frequency of a precisely fixed oscillator coupled to the atomic system between the pole faces of a magnet the field of which can be varied. When H corresponds to the resonance conditions given above, a sharp drop in current flowing through the coils of the a.c. system coupled to the atomic system is observed. From the value of H obtained in this fashion, g can be determined. Usually some reference substance is used in a null-method procedure.

The ESR method (also termed "EPR" from "electron paramagnetic resonance") informs the observer about the presence of unpaired electrons but does not identify the environment in which they occur, except under well-defined conditions. Any deviation of g from its value in the free-electron case can be interpreted unambiguously only when the nature of the atoms in which the electron finds itself is known. The relation of ESR signals in chloroplasts to triplet states of chlorophyll, or to other components of the photosynthetic machinery, is a problem for future work to elucidate. The related techniques of nuclear magnetic resonance (NMR), including the examination of proton resonance signals, is much farther from direct application to the study of chloroplast function because definitive studies require relatively high concentrations of reactants in well-defined systems. However, the rapid development of NMR techniques for application to problems in organic analysis and structure of pure compounds may yield important results for the elucidation of chemical processes in photosynthesis.

Insofar as the events from pt_s 15 to pt_s 4 are concerned, it is to be hoped that ESR and NMR techniques will provide an insight into the relative importance of free-radical intermediates in the energy storage process. It may be of interest that attempts have been made to detect the presence of free radicals in photosynthesizing algae by chemical methods. Thus, N. Uri (95a) examined oxygen evolution in the absence and presence of methyl methacrylate monomer—an indicator which polymerizes in the presence of free radicals. He found no polymer formation despite vigorous oxygen evolution in the chloroplast suspensions investigated, and concluded that if radicals were present they were of the type that terminate, rather than promote, formation of long-chain polymers.

I. "Wet" and "Dry" Chlorophylls

It has been noted (see p. 98 and Fig. 13) that solvent effects are important in alteration of the term levels of chlorophyll spectra. Thus, Livingston and his co-workers (96, 97) showed that chlorophyll in pure dry hydrocarbon solvents was much less fluorescent than in "wet" solvent systems. The presence of as little as 0.01% of a hydroxyl-containing component (alcohol, water, etc.) brought the fluorescence intensity up to the usual approximate value of 25%.

The suspicion that the disappearance of fluorescence at a given wavelength might be correlated with the appearance of a new emission band elsewhere in the spectrum was prevalent for some time, but a positive demonstration was provided only recently when J. Fernandez and R. S. Becker (34) showed that carefully dried chlorophylls *a* and *b* in a "glassy" hydrocarbon solvent such as 3-methylpentane, at liquid nitrogen temperature and in concentrations $\sim 10^{-4}$ *M*, showed strong fluorescences at 755 and 733 mμ, respectively. They found q_F values which were comparable with those for the normal emission in wet solvents at 673 mμ. Corresponding to these fluorescence emissions, these workers also noted a shoulder on the red side of the main absorption band. Both of these new spectral characteristics disappeared upon addition of hydroxylic solvents. For the new fluorescence of chlorophyll *a* at liquid nitrogen temperatures, $\tau_{1/2}$ was determined to be $\geq 5 \times 10^{-4}$ sec, an estimate being given as 10^{-3} sec.

The disappearance of the new absorption band upon addition of ethanol, evidenced as a shift toward the blue and into the main red absorption band of chlorophylls *a* and *b*, fulfilled one of the criteria mentioned (see p. 96) for assignment as an *n*-π transition. The characteristically large shift in fluorescence frequencies from 755 to 673 mμ, together with the long half-life of the 755 mμ fluorescence, suggested assignment of this new long wavelength to an n-π singlet-triplet interaction. At room temperatures, the intensity of this n-π singlet-triplet dropped markedly, a fact in accord with the expected conversion of triplet states back to singlets by collision with solvent and consequent reappearance of the normal singlet-singlet fluorescence. The importance of such solvent effects on spectral characteristics as a basis for the understanding of crepuscular components is obvious.

J. Delayed Singlet-Singlet Emission ("Chemiluminescence")

Another phenomenon of some importance in evaluation of mechanisms which operate in the era is the low-intensity delayed light emission observed in all photosynthetic organisms and discovered in 1951 by B. L. Strehler and W. Arnold (98). This luminescence appears to consist of at least two components, one of which has a half-life in the range of milliseconds, the other a half-life many orders of magnitude greater. This fascinating phenomenon—a delay in singlet-singlet emission which results in a change of $\tau_{1/2}$ from 10^{-9} sec to $\sim 10^{-3}$ sec and greater—could be interpreted as a simple reversal of photosynthesis. Extensive investigations have revealed the following facts (99, 100).

The emission is that of the normal singlet-singlet fluorescence. The action spectrum for excitation of luminescence is the same as that for photosynthesis. Its intensity is $\sim 10^{-3}$ to 10^{-5} that of normal photosynthetic fluorescence so that extremely sensitive photomultipliers are required to sense it. It increases with increasing intensity of illumination and eventually saturates just as does the photosynthetic process. Heating at 45°–50° C for a few minutes destroys it. The temperature optimum of 37° C is that for many enzymatic processes. Metabolic inhibitors effect strong changes in the luminescence. Treatments which depress green plant photosynthesis, e.g., elevated carbon dioxide pressures and anaerobic conditions, also inhibit luminescence. Chloroplasts show luminescence. Inhibition or loss of ability to carry out the Hill reaction causes a parallel loss of luminescence.

All of these facts suggest that the process is enzymatically controlled and an obligate feature of photosynthesis, rather than a side reaction of the type well-known to occur in model systems such as the porphyrin- or chlorophyll-catalyzed decomposition of peroxides (101). Another view (65, 102) is that the delayed emission results from recombination of photoelectrons with positive holes, when the electrons, originally ejected from chlorophyll, return to the trap created by the positive holes, as in a semiconductor-type mechanism. These electrons, which would be lost from the semiconductivity process advocated by the solid-state theory adherents (see p. 118, 136), would be part of the integral process of charge separation with resultant creation of the reducing and oxidizing systems which inaugurate biochemistry. Others (42, 102), who hold that semiconductivity is parasitic in the photosynthetic process, suggest that the luminescence may accompany photosynthesis but has no effect other than to lower q_P.

V. The Whole Picture

In this chapter, I have discussed some of the data available for a reconstruction of events in the era of radiation physics. Beginning with the older physiological experiments (54), and continuing through all the researches on polarization of fluorescence, fluorescence yields, etc., it appears that the mass of evidence is overwhelming in indicating that the primary absorption act is effective in initiating photosynthesis in a relatively small fraction (10^{-2}–10^{-3}) of the absorber chlorophyll molecules. By pt_s 15, the initial absorption act in a given chlorophyll is ended. This includes the rapid internal conversion from the initial excited singlet state. If absorption occurs in an accessory pigment, heterogeneous resonance transfer to a nearby chlorophyll follows in a time sufficiently small to accord with efficiencies up to 80%, or even 100%, according to the findings of L. N. M. Duysens and F. W. J. Teale, among others.

What happens next? Here there are the beginnings of controversy. The excited chlorophyll is either in the lowest-lying excited singlet or triplet state. One must expect transfer of excitation to a chlorophyll in a reactive site. The mechanisms available have been described; they are the strongly coupled ("fast") type discussed under the heading of "exciton migration," and the weakly coupled ("slow") type, termed "inductive resonance." Either process is adequate, and there are no data which compel abandonment of one or the other. One can examine briefly the arguments for each.

Phenomena which are characteristic of a semiconductor system in which exciton migration occurs have been noted in frozen, dry chloroplast films (65) and in reconstructed layered dye systems (67). These are temperature-induced luminescence and photoconductivity. In addition, W. Arnold and R. K. Clayton (103) have observed reversible shifts in the absorption spectra of both chromatophores and intact cell suspensions of the photosynthetic bacterium, *Rhodopseudomonas spheroides,* which they interpret as a lowering of ground-state energy of bacteriochlorophyll by the presence of electric fields which arise from charge separation in the wake of exciton dissociation into electrons and positive holes. Although the resistance to current flow of the dried chromatophore film is so high as to cast doubt on the suggestion that a true semiconductor system exists, they feel an adequate explanation for the low conductivity lies in the structure of the films. They assume that electrons experience difficulty in jumping from one chromatophore to another through protein layers. They place more emphasis on the fact that there is a sharp change in dielectric constant, which occurs on illumination, associated with an increased current (decreased resistance). This argues for a separation, upon illumination, of positive and negative charges which are free to move within any given chromatophore under the influence of an applied external field. When illumination ceases, they observe accumulation of charge to the original dark value which should follow from the disappearance of charge carriers by recombination. In addition, Arnold and Clayton observe that in the intact cells the spectral shifts in bacteriochlorophyll absorption are missing, and only shifts in cytochrome spectra appear (see Chapter IV). Thus, function of the photosynthetic machinery abolishes the charge separation phenomena, as expected if the electrons and holes produced by exciton dissociation are channeled to the photosynthetic hydrogen donors and acceptors. As additional evidence, they cite the reappearance of all the spectral shifts for bacteriochlorophyll in cells inhibited by azide and hydroxylamine. Finally, the delayed light emission, discussed in the previous section, is assumed to be merely the re-emission of excitation energy resulting from return of electrons in the conduction band to the valence bands of the chromatophore bacteriochlorophyll system.

A. N. Terenin and E. K. Putseiko (68a) reach similar conclusions about the reality of semiconductor phenomena in aggregates of the photosynthetic pigments. They conclude that release of an electron from an excited molecule is followed by its capture in a trap with consequent hole migration to a boundary layer where the holes are filled by electron donors. This mechanism provides a picture in which chlorophyll layers in contact with solution containing oxidants generate surface electron traps at the interfaces which can capture photoelectrons liberated at the interface to create negative charges. Positive holes formed in this fashion travel to the other boundaries and create positive charges. However, these workers leave open the question of the extent to which such processes occur during photosynthesis.

An opposed point of view is that all of these "semiconductivity" phenomena are parasitic processes which emerge only when photosynthesis is inhibited or absent. This view is based on cogent arguments too numerous to relate here [see, for instance, the presentations of J. Franck and his

co-workers (31, 102) or of G. Weber (42)]. Mainly, the argument runs that movement of excitation energy by inductive
resonance transfer affords a completely adequate explanation for all the phenomena noted. On the other hand, many
assumptions of an *ad hoc* nature must be made, and many
lacunae in data must be ignored, before the exciton picture
can be applied. A major difficulty is the absence of quantitative measurements of quantum yields for the charge separation process.

For the present summary, one can adopt the viewpoint
that inductive resonance transfer is all that is needed as a
working hypothesis and leave to the future the resolution
of the question whether exciton migration occurs as a major
feature of the primary energy conversion process. If one
supposes that the number of reactive sites is $\sim 10^{-2}$ that of
the total chlorophyll molecules in chloroplasts or chromatophores, then the number of transfers required on the basis
of a random walk from chlorophyll to chlorophyll would be
$\sim 10^4$. These would have to occur before 10^{-9} sec, the
natural emissive lifetime. There are many experimental
observations on fluorescence from organic scintillators which
show that this number of transfers can occur in the period
before pt_s 9. It is instructive to take a little space for the
presentation of one example.

G. T. Wright (104) measured values of q_F for anthracene
and naphthalene in pure and mixed crystals of these two
compounds, when excited by UV radiation ($\lambda = 254$ mμ),
and compared the decrease in q_F for naphthalene with that
observed for excitation by passage of 5 Mev alpha particles
(105). The relative concentrations of anthracene were no
higher than 10^{-3} moles per mole of naphthalene per liter
M/M_{naph}. Both modes of excitation gave the same values for
q_F, as the relative concentrations of anthracene were varied
from 10^{-3} to 10^{-8} M/M_{naph}. The fluorescence of the naphthalene ($q_F = 0.7$ at 10^{-8} M anthracene "impurity") dimin-
ished progressively to zero at 10^{-3} M anthracene, while q_F
for the anthracene rose correspondingly to 0.9, its normal
value in the pure state. This quenching of naphthalene

fluorescence occurred in the same manner by either mode of excitation, photon or alpha particle.

When alpha particles irradiate an organic crystal, they produce damage by insertion of flaws which act as non-radiative dissipative centers. Impurities, such as anthracene, would act in the same manner. Thus, it was expected and confirmed that the decrease in q_F for naphthalene due to radiation damage would follow a course similar to that found for the decrease in q_F of naphthalene with increasing anthracene content.

Wright needed to know the probability, P, for excitation energy transfer to a solute molecule in order to calculate the q_F expected for naphthalene. Supposing the inductive resonance mechanism to be operative, then, if v was the mean frequency of transfer among N naphthalene molecules, of which n were anthracene molecules, it followed that $P = v(n/N)$. The value of v could be estimated as close to the mean frequency of thermal vibrations because the probability of transfer was greatest when this was the case (53). From data in the literature, $v = 1.5 \times 10^{12}$. Additional data needed to calculate q_F for each component were the probabilities in unit time for fluorescence and for non-radiative dissipation. These could be obtained from measured values of decay times and fluorescence yields, given in the literature as 1.3×10^{-8} sec (106) and 0.9 (107), respectively, for anthracene, and 3.5×10^{-6} sec (108) and 0.7 (107), respectively, for naphthalene. If at time zero there were S_0 molecules of naphthalene excited, and if p, k, and P were probabilities for fluorescence, nonradiative loss, and transfer to anthracene, respectively, then the total lumines-cence for anthracene was given by the expression $p_{(anth)}PS_0/[p_{(anth)} + k_{(anth)}]\ [p_{(naph)} + k_{(naph)} + P]$, and the total lu-minescence for naphthalene was given by the expression $p_{(naph)}S_0/[p_{(naph)} + k_{(naph)} + P]$. Using the experimental values given, and the value for P, as given above and based on the inductive resonance mechanism, the values calculated for q_F coincided exactly with those measured.

Then Wright proceeded to calculate the number of nonradiative dissipative centers produced in naphthalene by an alpha particle (equivalent in effect to inclusion of an anthracene impurity). If this number was s, then in unit volume of the crystal lattice, a dose, D, of alpha particles would produce Ds/R nonradiative dissipative centers, where R was the alpha particle range. Substitution of Ds/R for n in the expression $P = vn/N$ gave the curve for quenching by radiation damage. Comparison with the experimental curves enabled a direct determination of s, which was found to be $\sim 2 \times 10^4$.

Hence, we see that in the $\sim 10^{-9}$ sec of excitation time available in these organic crystals, $\sim 10^4$ transfers could and did take place. Data such as these indicate that in systems quite analogous to what one expects in the chloroplast or chromatophore, an inductive resonance mechanism is all that is necessary; in fact, it seems obligatory. It is difficult to see how it could be avoided in any ordered aggregation of chlorophyll molecules. A discussion of this mechanism by J. Franck and R. L. Livingston (109), with particular reference to biological systems, should be consulted by the reader.

Some murkiness enters when one inquires next whether the fate of the excitation energy is to create eventually a singlet- or a triplet-state chlorophyll at the reactive sites. No problem exists with regard to energy transfer to reactive sites whether by migration through a system of singlet-state molecules or through triplet-state molecules. But once the migration is ended, what is the state of the chlorophyll from which photochemistry commences? J. Franck, J. L. Rosenberg, and C. Weiss (32) suggest that an answer can be obtained from the consideration that the ratio of q_F in the absence of photosynthesis to that found at optimal photosynthesis in certain green plants is two. They reason that if only the lowest excited singlet state were involved in the two reactions required by the Emerson enhancement effect and by the quantum yield data, then this ratio should be high. If only the triplet state is available, then fluorescence emission from the singlet would be competitive only with the radiationless transition from the triplet state, and not with photosynthesis from the triplet state. Thus, the ratio would be unity. Because it is actually two, these authors argue that half the photochemical acts go from the singlet directly and half from the triplet.

Be this as it may, more questions keep crowding in as one moves toward pt_s 9. It is necessary to know in what physicochemical environment the reactive chlorophylls are, as well as in what excited states they may be. One may suppose with the Brodys (74) that the reactive centers contain chlorophyll as both monomers and dimers and that these are the basis for a two-quantum process. Or one may accept the proposal of Franck (31) that the chlorophyll at the reactive site is modified in that it is "unprotected" from water, whereas most of the chlorophylls are "protected" in lipid surroundings. He then proposes that the two steps of the process at the reactive site involve first, the use of the excitation energy in the triplet state to collect reactants in a photochemical act, and second, the production of oxygen from water in a subsequent reaction with a minimal energy of activation. Details of this proposal will be presented in the next chapter. Another proposal submitted by various authors (110) suggests formation of adducts between chlorophyll and cytochromes or heme proteins.

There seems to be a growing conviction that the primary process in chromatophores requires only single-quantum excitation, rather than double-, as in chloroplasts, and that this lowered requirement correlates with the absence of oxygen evolution in bacteria. The data so far, while preliminary, are offered by J. M. Olson (see p. 63) who found (111) that in *Chromatium*, the photooxidation of cytochrome, which is an early reaction in bacterial photosynthesis (see Chapter IV), proceeds with a quantum efficiency which approaches one electron per photon, and that this efficiency is the same throughout the whole infrared absorption band for bacteriochlorophyll (802–908 mμ). Thus, there is no drop-off in efficiency on the long wavelength side of the same infrared absorption maximum. In this connection, it is also significant that M. Brody and H. Linschitz, in their experiments on fluorescence of various photosynthetic systems as monitored by the appearance of the new emission band at 720 mμ (80), find only one fluorescent species of bacteriochlorophyll (see p. 123). They are unable to state whether this is a monomer or dimer.

If one assumes that the primary act in photosynthetic bacteria is only a one-quantum process, then a scheme which includes suggestions from several authors (42, 99, 110) could be formulated for chromatophore history in the radiation physics era, as follows.

First, excitation of the bacteriochlorophyll (BChl) occurs (pt_s 15) as in reaction (1):

$$\text{BChl}_{\uparrow\downarrow} + h\nu \rightarrow \text{BChl}_{\uparrow}^{\downarrow}, _{\uparrow}^{\uparrow} \qquad \text{(or BChl*, for both species)} \qquad (1)$$

Then inductive resonance or exciton migration without dissociation follows to a site where BChl forms an adduct with cytochrome, viz.:

$$\text{BChl*} \rightarrow \text{BChl*} \cdot \text{Cyt} \qquad (pt_s \sim 15 \text{ to } 10) \qquad (2)$$

The reader is reminded that quenching of fluorescence in photosynthesis indicates effective competition for excitation energy before the characteristic time $pt_s \sim 9$, so that reaction (2) should be completed well before pt_s 9 and fills the period between pt_s 15 and pt_s 10. The introduction of the adduct pair serves two purposes. First, if an exciton mechanism is involved, it facilitates dissociation at the reactive site, so that an electron is available for further transport or reaction. Second, if an inductive resonance mechanism is involved, then the quenching mechanism follows by electron transfer, as in reaction (3).

$$\text{BChl*} \cdot \text{Cyt} \rightarrow \text{BChl}^- \cdot \text{Cyt}^+ \qquad (3)$$

This completes the history of chromatophore photosynthesis up to $pt_s \sim 9$. However, if the electron comes from exciton dissociation, then the hole reacts with the cytochrome and the electron with the bacteriochlorophyll, as in reaction (4).

$$\text{BChl*} \cdot \text{Cyt} + \epsilon^- + \oplus \rightarrow \text{BChl}^- \cdot \text{Cyt}^+ \qquad (4)$$

The electron-rich $BChl^-$ species can donate its electron to an acceptor, A, close by. Alternatively, the electron from exciton dissociation may come to rest, by a process of electron exchange, on a BChl some distance removed from the original excited $BChl^* \cdot Cyt$ adduct, i.e.,

$$A + BChl^* \cdot Cyt + BChl + \epsilon^- + \oplus \rightarrow BChl^- \cdot A + BChl \cdot Cyt^+ \qquad (4')$$

The system returns to its initial state when the $BChl^-$ reduces A and the electrons from the external hydrogen donor required in bacterial photosynthesis reach $BChl \cdot Cyt^+$. Short-term delayed light emission could arise from reversal of this scheme starting at (4). Long-term delayed light emission could occur when electrons, trapped as in (4'), slowly diffuse to an available hole.

This scheme is less applicable to green plant photosynthesis because there is no certainty about the nature of the adduct, if any, and there is a need to know details of chemistry (events in $pt_s < 9$). Thus, the manner in which two independent quantum events are integrated to produce the oxygen characteristic of green plant photosynthesis, while setting the stage for all the events of the biochemical era ($pt_s \leq 4$), is wholly unclear. These matters will be considered again in the next chapter.

Many topics touched upon in this chapter require much more intensive treatment than has been given them. A number of references included in the bibliography of this chapter, in addition to the general references cited in Chapter I, will be helpful; among them are references (1), (3), (4), (5), (14), (19), (29), (30), and (53). In addition, there are the monographs by L. Reid, "Excited States in Chemistry and Biology," Academic Press, New York (1957); and by M. Kasha, "Molecular Electronic Structure," McGraw-Hill, New York (1960). Three recent texts on molecular spectra are the following:

1. B. Bak, "Elementary Introduction to Molecular Spectra," 2nd ed. Wiley (Interscience), New York (1962).

2. R. P. Bauman, "Absorption Spectra," Wiley, New York (1962).

3. G. Barrow, "Molecular Spectroscopy," McGraw-Hill, New York (1962).

References*

1. J. C. Slater and N. H. Frank, "Introducton to Theoretical Physics," p. 445ff. McGraw-Hill, New York, 1933.
2. J. C. Slater and N. H. Frank (1), p. 111ff.
3. W. Kauzmann, "Quantum Chemistry," p. 581ff. Academic Press, New York, 1957.
4. G. Herzberg, "Atomic Spectra and Atomic Structure," p. 120ff. Dover Press, New York, 1944.
5. P. Pringsheim, "Fluorescence and Phosphorescence," p. 313ff. Interscience, New York, 1949.
6. G. N. Lewis and M. Kasha, *J. Am. Chem. Soc.* **67,** 994 (1945).
7. R. Ladenburg, *Verhandl. deut. physik. Ges.* **16,** 765 (1914).
8. E. Gaviola, *Z. Physik.* **42,** 853 (1927).
9. E. A. Bailey, Jr., and G. K. Rollefson, *J. Chem. Phys.* **21,** 1315 (1953).
10. O. D. Dimitrievsky, V. L. Ermolaev, and A. N. Terenin, *Doklady Akad. Nauk S.S.S.R.* **114,** 751 (1957).
11. S. S. Brody and E. Rabinowitch, *Science* **125,** 555 (1957).
12. P. Latimer, T. T. Bannister, and E. Rabinowitch, *Science* **124,** 585 (1956).
13. G. Weber and F. W. J. Teale, *Trans. Faraday Soc.* **53,** 646 (1957).
14. T. Förster, "Fluorescenz Organischer Verbindungen." Vanden Hoek and Ruprecht, Gottinger, 1951.
15. F. P. Zxcheile and C. L. Comar, *Botan. Gaz.* **102,** 463 (1941).
16. R. J. P. Williams, *Chem. Revs.* **56,** 299 (1956).
17. R. J. P. Williams, *in* "The Enzymes" (P. D. Boyer, H. Lardy, and K. Myrbäck, eds.), Vol. I, p. 391 et seq. Academic Press, New York, 1952.
18. R. J. P. Williams, *in* "Symposium on Haematin Enzymes" (J. E. Falk, P. Lemberg, and R. K. Morton, eds.), p. 41 et seq. Pergamon Press, New York, 1961.
19. An excellent recent presentation of molecular orbital theory will be found in A. Streitwieser, Jr., "Molecular Orbital Theory for Organic Chemists." Wiley, New York, 1961.
20. W. T. Simpson, *J. Chem. Phys.* **17,** 1218 (1949).
21. H. C. Longuet-Higgins, C. W. Rector, and J. R. Platt, *J. Chem. Phys.* **18,** 1174 (1950).

* Complete information pertaining to symposium references [1] to [7] and general references I, II, and III can be found in Section VI (Collateral Reading) of Chapter I.

22. J. R. Platt, *in* "Radiation Biology" (A. Hollaender, ed.), Vol. III, Ch. 2. McGraw-Hill, New York, 1956.

23. M. Gouterman, *J. Chem. Phys.* **30,** 1139 (1959).

24. M. Gouterman, *J. Chem. Phys.* **33,** 1523 (1960).

25. E. Rabinowitch, *Revs. Modern Phys.* **16,** 226 (1944).

26. S. Granick and H. Gilder, *Advances in Enzymol.* **7,** 305 (1947).

27. H. L. McMurry and R. S. Mulliken, *Proc. Natl. Acad. Sci. U.S.* **26,** 312 (1940).

28. M. Kasha, symposium ref. [7], p. 31 et seq.

29. L. E. Orgel, "An Introductory to Transition-Metal Chemistry Ligand-Field Theory." Methuen, London, 1960.

30. L. Pauling, "The Nature of the Chemical Bond," 3rd ed. Cornell Univ. Press, New York, 1961.

31. J. Franck, *Proc. Natl. Acad. Sci. U.S.* **44,** 941 (1958).

32. J. Franck, J. L. Rosenberg, and C. Weiss, *in* "Luminescence of Organic and Inorganic Materials" (H. P. Kallman and G. M. Spruch, eds.), p. 11 et seq. Wiley, New York.

33. P. S. Stensby and J. L. Rosenberg, *J. Phys. Chem.* **65,** 906 (1961).

34. J. Fernandez and R. S. Becker, *J. Chem. Phys.* **31,** 467 (1959).

35. I. S. Singh and R. S. Becker, *J. Am. Chem. Soc.* **82,** 2083 (1960).

36. J. C. Goedheer, *Nature* **176,** 928 (1955).

37. M. Moscowitz, *in* "Optical Rotatory Dispersion" (C. Djerassi, ed.). Chapter 12. McGraw-Hill, New York, 1960.

38. R. Becker and M. Abraham, "Theorie d. Electrizitat." Teubner, Leipzig, 1933.

39. J. C. Goedheer, Doctoral Dissertation, Utrecht (1957), Chapter 2.

40. A classic essay by F. Perrin, *Ann. Phy.* **12,** 169 (1929), should be read for an unusually clear exposition of fluorescence phenomena.

41. R. Stupp and H. Kuhn, *Helv. Chim. Acta* **35,** 2469 (1952).

42. G. Weber, Symposium ref. [5], p. 395 et seq.

43. G. Weber, and F. J. W. Teale, *Trans. Faraday Soc.* **54,** 640 (1958).

44. G. Weber, *Biochem. J.* **47,** 114 (1950).

45. L. N. M. Duysens and G. H. M. Kronenberg, *Biochim. et Biophys. Acta* **26,** 437 (1957).

46. P. D. Boyer and H. Theorell, *Acta Chem. Scand.* **10,** 447 (1956).

47. W. F. Watson, *Trans. Faraday Soc.* **48,** 526 (1952).

48. G. Weber, *Nature* **180,** 1409 (1957).

49. A. S. Holt and E. E. Jacobs, *Am. J. Botany,* **41,** 710 (1954).

50. S. Ainsworth and E. Rabinowitch, *Science* **131,** 303 (1960).

51. R. Emerson and W. Arnold, *J. Gen. Physiol.* **15,** 391 (1932).

52. T. Forster, *Ann. Physik* **2,** 55 (1948).

53. N. F. Mott and H. J. W. Massey, "Theory of Atomic Collisions." Oxford Univ. Press (Clarendon), London and New York, 1952.

54. G. Weber, *Trans. Faraday Soc.* **50,** 552 (1954).

55. F. W. J. Teale, *Biochim. et Biophys. Acta* **42,** 69 (1960).

56. S. S. Brody, *Z. f. Electrochem.* 64, 187 (1960).
57. A. N. Terenin and V. L. Ermolaev, *Trans. Faraday Soc.* 52, 1042 (1956).
58. L. N. M. Duysens, *Nature* 168, 548 (1951).
59. H. J. Dutton, W. M. Manning, and B. M. Duggar, *J. Phys. Chem.* 47, 308 (1943).
60. E. C. Wassink and J. A. H. Kersten, *Enzymologia* 12, 3 (1946).
61. J. C. Goedheer, *Biochem. et Biophys. Acta* 35, 1 (1959).
62. C. Bril, *Biochim. et Biophys. Acta* 39, 296 (1960).
63. J. Frenkel, *Phys. Rev.* 37, 17, 1276 (1931).
64. G. Scheibe, *Naturwissenschaften* 26, 412 (1938).
65. W. Arnold and H. K. Sherwood, *Proc. Natl. Acad. Sci. U.S.* 43, 105 (1957).
66. E. Katz, *in* "Photosynthesis in Plants" (J. Franck and W. E. Loomis, eds.), p. 287 et seq. Iowa State College Press, Ames, Iowa, 1949.
67. M. Calvin, *J. Theoret. Biol.* 1, 258 (1961); also symposium ref. [7], p. 317 et seq.
68. D. R. Kearns and M. Calvin, *J. Am. Chem. Soc.* 83, 2110 (1961).
68a. See A. N. Terenin and E. K. Putseiko, *Proc. 5th Intern. Congr. Biochem.*, (Moscow) Symposium VI, Pergamon Press, New York, in press (1962), for a review.
69. H. Kallmann and M. Pope, *J. Chem. Phys.* 30, 585 (1959).
70. H. Kallmann and M. Pope, *Nature* 185, 753 (1960).
71. A. A. Krasnovsky, K. K. Voinovskaya and L. M. Kosobutskaya, *Doklady Akad. Nauk S.S.S.R.* 85, 389 (1952).
72. A. A. Krasnovsky and L. M. Kosobutskaya, *Doklady Akad. Nauk S.S.S.R.* 91, 343 (1953).
73. S. S. Brody, *Science* 128, 838 (1958).
74. S. S. Brody and M. Brody, *Biochim. et Biophys. Acta* 54, 495 (1961).
75. J. Lavorel, *J. Phys. Chem.* 61, 1864 (1957).
76. T. Forster and K. Kasper, *Z. Phys. Chem. (Frankfurt)* [N.S.] 1, 275 (1954).
77. W. F. Watson and R. L. Livingston, *J. Chem. Phys.* 18, 802 (1950).
78. F. Rodrigo, Doctoral Thesis, Univ. of Utrecht (1955).
79. S. French and V. K. Young, General ref. III, p. 343.
80. W. L. Butler, *Arch. Biochem. Biophys.* 93, 413 (1961).
80a. M. Brody and H. Linschitz, *Science* 133, 705 (1961).
81. J. Franck, *Ann. Rev. Plant Physiol.* 2, 53 (1951).
82. E. Rabinowitch, general ref. I, Vol. 3, Chapter 35.
83. R. L. Livingston, general ref. II, part 1, p. 849 et seq.
84. E. W. Abrahamson and H. Linschitz, *J. Chem. Phys.* 23, 2198 (1955).
85. H. Linschitz and K. Sarkanen, *J. Am. Chem. Soc.* 80, 4827 (1958).
86. G. Porter, *Proc. Roy. Soc.* A208, 284 (1950), see also, symposium ref. [7], p. 69 et seq.

87. A. Weller, *J. Am. Chem. Soc.* **76**, 5819 (1954).

88. H. Linschitz and L. Pekkarinen, *J. Am. Chem. Soc.* **82**, 2411 (1960).

89. G. N. Lewis and M. Calvin, *J. Am. Chem. Soc.* **67**, 1232 (1945).

90. C. A. Hutchison, Jr. and B. W. Mangum, *J. Chem. Phys.* **29**, 952 (1958).

91. C. A. Hutchison, Jr. and B. W. Mangum, *J. Chem. Phys.* **32**, 1261 (1960).

92. B. Commoner, J. J. Heise and J. Townsend, *Proc. Natl. Acad. Sci.* U.S. **42**, 710 (1956); see also, symposium ref. [7], p. 357 et seq.

93. G. Tollin, P. B. Sogo, and M. Calvin, *Ann. N.Y. Acad. Sci.* **74**, 310 (1958); see also *J. Chem. Phys.* **55**, 919 (1958).

94. M. B. Allen, L. H. Piette, and J. C. Murchio, *Biochem. Biophys. Research Communs.* **4**, 271 (1961).

95. For an excellent review, see J. E. Wertz, *Chem. Revs.* **55**, 829 (1955).

95a. N. Uri, *Biochim. et Biophys. Acta* **18**, 209 (1955).

96. R. L. Livingston, W. F. Watson, and J. McArdle, *J. Am. Chem. Soc.* **71**, 1542 (1949).

97. R. L. Livingston and S. A. Weil, *Nature* **170**, 750 (1950).

98. B. L. Strehler and W. Arnold, *J. Gen. Physiol.* **34**, 809 (1951).

99. B. L. Strehler, symposium ref. [3], p. 118 et seq.; also *Proc. 5th Intern. Cong. Biochem., Moscow, 1961* in press.

100. W. Arnold and J. B. Davidson, *J. Gen. Physiol.* **37**, 677 (1954).

101. H. Linschitz, symposium ref. [7], p. 173 et seq.

102. J. E. Brugger and J. Franck, *Arch. Biochem. Biophys.* **75**, 465 (1958).

103. W. Arnold and R. K. Clayton, *Proc. Natl. Acad. Sci. U.S.* **46**, 769 (1960).

104. G. T. Wright, *Proc. Phys. Soc. (London)* **B68**, 241 (1955); **A66**, 777 (1953).

105. J. B. Birks and F. A. Black, *Proc. Phys. Soc. (London)* **A64**, 511 (1951).

106. S. H. Liebson, *Nucleonics* **10**, 41 (1952).

107. E. J. Bowen, E. Mikiewicz, and F. W. Smith, *Proc. Phys. Soc. (London)* **A62**, 26 (1949).

108. S. H. Liebson, M. E. Bishop and J. O. Elliot, *Phys. Rev.* **80**, 907 (1950).

109. J. Franck and R. L. Livingston, *Revs. Modern Phys.* **21**, 505 (1949).

110. M. D. Kamen, symposium ref. [7], p. 483 et seq.; also I.U.B. Sympos., "Biological Structure and Function," First IUB/IUBS Intern. Syymposium, Stockholm, 1960 (T. W. Goodwin and O. Lindberg eds.), p. 277 et seq. Pergamon Press, New York 1961.

111. J. M. Olson, private communication.

CHAPTER IV

The Era of Photochemistry: pt_s 9 to pt_s 4

I. Generalities

Knowledge about events in this era is so scanty as to recall the admonition of Wittgenstein: "Whereof one cannot speak, thereof one must be silent." Nevertheless, the reader should be aware of certain selections of data culled from various areas of research which will be considered briefly in this chapter.

There is little reason to doubt that, in chloroplasts and chromatophores, chemical reactions in this era are consummated between reactants rigidly embedded in condensed multilayered systems bathed in semiliquid media which provide links with the rest of the cellular mass. Such reactions are unlikely to be diffusion controlled and may have abnormally low activation energies because the reactants are always in contact. Geometry will be a deciding factor. Thus, there will be little or no resemblance to the conventional sort of chemistry encountered in solution.

If the time limit of pt_s 9 is considered, it is obvious that any chemical reactions which are directly effective in quenching chlorophyll fluorescence must run their course in pt_s 10 to 11. Such reactions, at least in solution, involve processes in which there is a redistribution of electrons and protons, and not of the more massive nuclei (1, 2). Studies of mechanisms in such extremely rapid processes have been elaborated greatly in recent years through the introduction of many new techniques, among which may be cited (a) the so-called "relaxation" methods, which depend on pulsed disturbances of equilibria brought about by sudden pressure, temperature, and volume changes; (*b*) photoflash methods (an aspect of which was discussed on p. 123); (*c*) magnetic resonance; and (*d*) polarography, as well as others (3). Of particular interest is the methodology based on fluorescence quenching to which attention will be directed briefly.

II. Fast Reactions of Excited Molecules as Revealed by Fluorescence Quenching

It has already been stated (Chapter III) that absorption of a photon will bring a molecule into its lowest excited singlet or multiplet state in pt_s 12 to 13. Transition back to the ground state will involve radiative processes (fluorescence, phosphorescence), deactivation by collision processes, and nonradiative stabilization as new chemical species. It is the last of these possibilities that is of major interest because it affords eventually the only means of useful photochemical energy storage. Hence, it may be inquired what reactions can be initiated from the excited state and how they differ from those expected to follow thermal activation in conventional chemical processes. These differences can be studied by examination of changes in absorption and emission of radiation brought about by a variety of experimental conditions (4). Four kinds of reaction are amenable to this approach. If one denotes by A a reactive species in the ground state, by A* the same species in the excited state, and by X a reaction partner, then equilibria can be represented as follows:

(*1*) Complex-formation:

$$A + X \rightleftharpoons A \cdot X$$
$$A^* + X \rightleftharpoons A^* \cdot X$$

(*2*) Isomerization:

$$A^* \rightarrow A^*_{isomer}$$

(*3*) Protonation (acid-base) reactions:

$$A + HX \rightleftharpoons AH^+ + X^-, \quad \text{or } A^- + HX^+$$
$$A^* + HX \rightleftharpoons A^*H^+ + X^-, \quad \text{or } (A^*)^- + HX^+$$

(4) Charge (electron) transfer:

$$A + X \rightleftharpoons A^{\pm} + X^{\mp}$$
$$A^* + X \rightleftharpoons A^{*\pm} + X^{\mp}$$

Examples of all these types of reaction are known in which reaction rates are sufficiently great to give reaction times of the same or lesser magnitudes than the emissive lifetimes of the excited species.

In general, it can be expected that an excited molecule will differ in reactivity, perhaps very markedly, from the corresponding ground state form. As an example, consider the difference in degree of acidity exhibited by excited and ground state β-naphthol. A. Weller (5) has shown that the pK for the excited form is 2.5, whereas for the ground state it is 9.5. Very often it is found, as T. Förster first showed, that in aqueous solutions of aromatic hydroxy and ammonium compounds, the dissociation equilibrium in the excited state is established at proton concentrations six or more orders of magnitude greater than those for the ground state equilibrium (6).

These results can be obtained by absorption and fluorescence measurements at different pH values. To see the relation between radiation characteristics and pK, consider a very simplified system in which a molecule A reacts to form another molecule B in the presence of a reaction partner C. Suppose further that only the reactivities of A and A* relative to unexcited C are to be compared, and that reaction entropies are the same for both A and A*. It follows from well-known thermodynamic relations between the equilibrium constant, K, and reaction enthalpies, H, that $\ln K^*/K = (\Delta H - \Delta H^*)/RT$. It is easy to show (4) that $\Delta H - \Delta H^*$ is equal to the difference in frequency between absorption maxima at the various values of pH. A convenient form (4) of this relation is

$$pK^* = pK - (0.625/T)\Delta\nu$$

where $\Delta\nu$, the mean of spectral shifts in absorption and fluorescence maxima, is given in wave numbers. Thus, in the case of β-naphthol (4), $\Delta\nu$ is 3.36×10^3 cm^{-1}, pK is 9.46, so that for $T = 300°$ C, pK^* is ~ 2.7.

Reaction types (2) and (3) often involve intramolecular hydrogen bonding. For type (3) one may quote again from the article by A. Weller (4), who presents the case of salicylic acid esters (I) compared to *o*-methoxybenzoic acid esters (II) dissolved in methylcyclohexane, i.e.,

(I)   (II)

Although the absorption maxima for these two molecular types are displaced rather slightly, the fluorescence maximum of (I) is more than 500 wave numbers further in the red than that for (II). Moreover, (I) shows an additional low intensity fluorescence maximum at the same position as the fluorescence maximum for (II). It is reasonable to associate this low intensity maximum of (I) with the excited form in which no proton migration has occurred, i.e.,

(I)

because of its similarity to the only excited form of (II) possible, i.e.,

(II)

whereas the main fluorescence maximum of (I) can be assigned to a structure expected from a proton shift, i.e.,

Proton transfer, as a result of excitation, is well illustrated by the phenomena noted (7) when acridine dyes are mixed with carboxylic acids and excited at $-180°$ C by irradiation at $\lambda = 366$ mμ. The mixture exhibits initially the green fluorescence of acridine cation, i.e.,

Upon irradiation at $\lambda = 250$ mμ, the wavelength absorbed by the cation, the fluorescence changes to violet, characteristic of the neutral acridine, i.e.,

Complex formation is a very commonly encountered process. Often, there is no change in absorption although a considerable shift occurs in fluorescence maxima. Thus, in pyrene solutions (8), fluorescence at low concentrations with a maximum at approximately 25,700 cm^{-1} attenuates and is eventually replaced by a new maximum in concentrated solutions at approximately 21,000 cm^{-1}. Such behavior is characteristic of complex formation i.e., pyrene + pyrene → excited dimer, not only on the obvious grounds of concentration dependence but also because its rate is diffusion controlled. Shifts in absorption spectra often attend formation of complexes arising from hydrogen bonding (4).

However, complex formation sometimes occurs without any spectroscopic alterations. Thus, in the reversible photoreduction of thionine by ferrous ion, mentioned previously (p. 111), it is found (9) that the kinetic data obtained when studying quantum yields at varying concentrations of ferrous and ferric ions are best explained by assumption of two processes. One of these is conventional in that it supposes production of a long-lived excited thionine which is reduced by the diffusion-controlled reaction with ferrous ion. The other postulates excitation of a complex formed in the dark between the dye and ferrous ion, the presence of which is not indicated by a new absorption spectrum. A feature of this mechanism is that charge transfer occurs between the ferrous ion and the dye moiety in the excited complex, and this precedes dissociation of the complex into ferric ions and reduced dye.

The occurrence of charge transfer in complexes is a process which may be of particular significance for the chemical events in pt_s 9 to pt_s 4. Such a process has been noted as a possible mechanism in the quenching of bacteriochlorophyll fluorescence during chromatophore photosynthesis, the complex in this case being that between the bacteriochlorophyll and the bacterial cytochrome (Chapter III). Most of the data which bear on the existence of such processes are rather indirect, but a few examples may be cited. Thus, acridine fluorescence is quenched by amines; the fluorescence yields can be correlated with the ionization potential of the amine (4) Or, again, the quenching constant, k_4 (see p. 129), in the kinetic expression for the disappearance of the triplet state of porphyrins and aromatic hydrocarbons is not dependent on the magnetic moment of the quencher ion used, but seems rather to be related to the possibility of electron transfer. As cited previously (p. 129), Mn^{++}—a very strongly paramagnetic ion—is a rather poor quencher (10). The more important parameter is the degree of solvation, or complexing, of the ion. The assumption of a complex between the excited molecule and the quencher, followed by radiationless transitions to the ground state on the one hand, and by intermediate charge transfer on the other, with eventual return to the ground state, is illustrated in Fig. 11 in Chapter III, as taken from the discussion by H. Linschitz and L. Pekkarinen (10).

III. The Photochemistry of Chlorophyll

Reviews of the present status of knowledge about the photochemistry of chlorophyll are available in articles by R. S. Livingston (11) and A. A. Krasnovsky (12). All of the processes noted in the previous section are possible, together with many variations expected for molecules as complex as chlorophyll and its derivatives. The question to be decided by future research is not what is possible, but what actually occurs.

Ground-state chlorophyll itself is a reactive molecule as can be expected from the various groupings which are festooned around the basic porphin structure (see p. 26), such as the carbonyl carbon in the isocyclic ring (C-9), and the vinyl group substituted at C-2. The central metal ion, Mg^{++}, affords a site for formation of solvates.

The reactions known to occur *in vitro* are, in addition to complex formation (primarily with basic solvents), oxidations by ferric salts (13), polymerization (14, 15), and irreversible oxidation (typified by the well-known "phase test," which involves a transition from green to brown to green again when chlorophyll is treated with methanolic KOH).

In the elucidation of the phase test, the structure of the intermediates has been established by infrared analysis (16). It appears that there is formation of a negative ion in the isocyclic portion of chlorophyll, with the negative charge distributed on both the ketone and the ester carbonyl oxygen atoms as well as on C-10; thus, A. S. Holt writes the following canonical forms for the enolate anion as intermediate in the reaction of pheophytin *a*, viz.:

These findings are consistent with the fact that "allomerized" chlorophyll, i.e., chlorophyll slowly oxidized on standing in air, is unable to give a phase test, presumably because oxidation during allomerization occurs at C-10.

The special characteristic of the porphin nucleus is the system of alternating single and double bonds which present the labile π electrons for participation in a variety of oxidation-reduction processes. Thus, to give but one example, consider a corner of the tetrapyrrolic skeleton (17), as shown (*I*). This includes a nitrogen with an unshared pair of electrons (nonbonding)

(R)   (I)   (0)

which are available for formation of the semiquinoidal or half-oxidized form of the radical, (O). This radical, when formed in the chlorophyll structure, could be one possible form of the "oxidized" chlorophyll (Chl+) which apparently occurs when intact chloroplasts or chromatophores are treated with oxidizing agents such as permanganate or ferricyanide (see p. 61). An oxidizing potential of approximately 0.4–0.5 ev is proposed for (Chl+) based on the extent of bleaching of the chlorophyll when exposed to given concentrations of these oxidants (18). The bleaching is assumed to monitor the amount of the oxidized form, because the characteristic macrocyclic resonance structure responsible for the Soret band is hindered or abolished when electrons are removed from the bridge carbons, as shown.

The half-reduced form, (*R*) or (Chl⁻), is a powerful reducing agent. Its standard potential is estimated at approximately -1 ev on the basis of polarographic measurements (18a). Two different equilibria can be postulated; one involves $Chl \rightleftharpoons Chl^+ + \varepsilon^-$, with $E_m \sim +0.4$ to $+0.5$ ev, and another $Chl^- \rightleftharpoons Chl + \varepsilon^-$, with $E_m \sim -1.0$ ev. Thus, half-reduced chlorophyll is one volt more reducing than hydrogen gas under standard conditions, while half-oxidized chlorophyll is more oxidizing by about half a volt. In a dimer combination, Chl·Chl, removal of an electron from one of the pair and its placement on the other to form Chl⁻·Chl+ would be expected to require most of the energy in a single red quantum (approximately 1.5–1.8 ev). A difficulty in deciding whether Chl⁻ or Chl+ is formed on the basis of the bleaching phenomenon is that both forms could be associated with reduced optical absorbancy because in both forms there is hindered resonance at the bridge carbons. This difficulty has already been remarked upon in connection with the interpretation of photochemically excited changes in optical properties of chlorophyll *in vitro* and *in vivo* (see p. 62).

It is evident that excitation of chlorophyll can result in partial stabilization of these half-oxidized or half-reduced forms; which of these occurs depends on the electron affinities of the solvent used, the reactants present in adducts, etc. An examination of the literature on photochemical reactions of chlorophyll (11) reveals that no generalizations suitable for textbook presentation are possible. A partial list of the reactions which have been studied includes quenching of fluorescence by all varieties of oxidants and reductants, formation of radicals or ions, autooxidation, oxidation-reductions, pheophytinization, and chlorophyll sensitization of oxidations and reductions.

Perhaps the most interesting process is the reversible photoreduction first demonstrated by A. A. Krasnovsky (19) and since studied extensively by him and his colleagues, notably V. B. Evstigneev and G. P. Brin. In this reaction, chlorophyll or pheophytin, dissolved in air-free pyridine which contains an excess of ascorbic acid, is photochemically reduced in red light to a labile pink intermediate with a major absorption band maximum at 523 mμ. Partial regeneration of the chlorophyll is obtained by exposure to air in the dark. The nature of the solvent is critical. The best one of many tested is pyridine. In general, a basic solvent is required. It also appears that not all reducing agents are effective. In addition to chlorophyll *a* and pheophytin, other related compounds react, e.g., chlorophyll *b,* bacteriochlorophyll, protochlorophyll, allomerized chlorophyll, and magnesium phthalocyanin.

At least three long-lived products are formed, but nothing can be said with certainty about their structures. It is evident, however, that the primary product is not the pink intermediate observed visually (20). Thus, when the reaction mixture is illuminated and electrochemical potentials developed are measured (20), rapid changes in potential occur before spectral changes associated with the pink product(s) appear. Efforts to establish that proton transfer or electron transfer are involved have led to equivocal results (11, 21–23). The notion that a free radical could form, as expected on the basis of the imagery presented for formation of semiquinoidal forms (p. 155), has been disproved by the demonstration that no electron spin resonance signal is associated with the pink intermediate (24, 24a). S. S. Brody (25), studying the photoreduction process with phenylhydrazine as reductant, concludes from the fluorescence behavior of the products that the first stable product produced in the Krasnovsky system has an absorption maximum at 585 mμ. G. Zieger and H. T. Witt (26), using an impulse spectrophotometric technique (see next section), find that in the classic Krasnovsky system [chlorophyll-pyridine (15% water)-ascorbic acid], a rapid spectral shift occurs with formation of a short-lived intermediate ($\tau \sim 5 \times 10^{-2}$ sec) which has an absorption maximum at 475 mμ.

Chlorophyll-sensitized oxidations and reductions should provide model systems for rationalization of processes in the photochemical era. Unfortunately, evidence is still meagre and largely qualitative. In Table III, a summary of chlorophyll-sensitized reactions, taken in part from the review by Livingston (11) and expanded to include recent observations on cytochromes, is presented.

Interesting and significant extensions of these observations come from recent studies by L. P. Vernon (35a). He has noted that chlorophylls, pheophytins, porphyrins, and

Table III

SUMMARY OF CHLOROPHYLL-SENSITIZED OXIDATION-REDUCTION
REACTION

Oxidant	Reductant	Solvent	Reference
Azobenzene	Phenylhydrazine	Methanol	27
Butter yellow	Ascorbic acid	Methanol	27
Methyl red	Phenylhydrazine	Methanol	28
Methyl red	Ascorbic acid	Pyridine	25
Methyl red	Hydrazobenzene	Methanol	27
Methyl red	Semicarbazide·HCl	Methanol	27
Methyl red	tert.–Hexylmercaptan	Methanol + 0.05 M HCl	27
Methyl red	Phenyl-hydroxylamine	Methanol	27
Azo turkey red	Phenylhydrazine	Methanol + 0.05 M HCl	27
o-Dinitrobenzene	Phenylhydrazine	Ethanol	29
o-Dinitrobenzene	Ascorbic acid	Ethanol	29
Safranine–T	Ascorbic acid	Ethanol or pyridine	30
Safranine–T	Pyruvic acid	Ethanol or pyridine	31
Safranine–T	Sodium sulfide	Pyridine (+15% H_2O)	30
Riboflavin	Ascorbic acid	Ethanol or pyridine	30
Riboflavin	Sodium sulfide	Pyridine	30
Diphosphopyridine nucleotide (DPN)	Ascorbic acid	Pyridine	30
Diphosphopyridine nucleotide (DPN)	Sodium sulfide	Pyridine	30, 32
Triphenyltetrazolium chloride	Hydrazine	Methanol	33
Air	Ferrocytochrome c	Mixed phosphate buffer and ethanolic solutions	34, 35
Ferricytochrome c	Succinic, malic, lactic acids	Mixed phosphate buffer and ethanolic solutions	34, 35

phycocyanins can catalyze a slow but appreciable photoreduction of pyridine nucleotides and the dyes, methyl red
and tetrazolium blue, when ascorbate is the electron donor.
These reactions occur in aqueous media, e.g., in phosphate

buffer, pH 6–7, unlike those exhibited in Table III. The catalysis of DPN and TPN reduction requires the presence of the enzyme, pyridine nucleotide reductase (p. 33).

The oxidation-reduction processes which involve DPN and cytochrome c are of particular interest because substances closely related to these have been implicated as constituents of chloroplasts and chromatophores (see p. 33, 34), and because analogous reactions occur in chloroplasts and chromatophores. Krasnovsky (34) has suggested, following his general mechanism, that in the photoreduction of cytochrome c, a photochemical reduction of chlorophyll (Chl) at the expense of the hydrogen donor occurs first, i.e.,

$$Chl + AH \xrightarrow{h\nu} Chl^- + AH^+$$

followed by a dark reaction in which the reduced chlorophyll is oxidized by the ferricytochrome, i.e.,

$$Chl^- + Fe^{+++}_{cyto\ c} \rightarrow Chl + Fe^{++}_{cyto\ c}$$

In the photooxidation of cytochrome c, air is required. No direct light-activated electron transfer from ferrocytochrome to chlorophyll is noted, but he postulates it nevertheless, i.e.,

$$Chl + Fe^{++}_{cyto\ c} \xrightarrow{h\nu} Chl^- + Fe^{+++}_{cyto\ c}$$

This is the same reaction assumed to be a primary step in the chromatophore mechanism suggested in Chapter III (p. 142). Krasnovsky assumes that rapid dark reversal makes it impossible to see the electron transfer postulated, and that addition of air bleeds off Chl^- and shifts the equilibrium so that the oxidized cytochrome is observed to form. An obvious experimental approach yet to be undertaken is the use of flash spectrophotometry to detect simultaneous bleaching of the chlorophyll and oxidation of the ferrocytochrome under strictly anaerobic conditions. G. Zieger and H. T. Witt (35b) have made a beginning, by the use of flash spectrophotometry (see next section), to follow the fast absorption changes induced in chlorophyll a in the Krasnovsky system, as mentioned previously (p. 157).

IV. The Study of Reactions from pt_s 5 to pt_s 2 by Spectrophotometric Methods

The effects of illumination in chromatophores and chloroplasts involve minute changes in absorbancy brought about by changes in steady states of oxidation, aggregation, solvation, etc. when these systems are photoactivated. A major complication arises because it is usually necessary to use dense extracts or cell suspensions which scatter light and thus create artifacts at the measuring apparatus not related to the direct effect of the actinic light. The changes which interest us rarely exceed 10^{-3} absorbancy units, and these small changes must be monitored both in the steady state and in transient states with precisions of a few percent. The only practical approach is a differential method of some sort; a number have been devised in recent years which have achieved notable success in demonstration of absorbancy changes brought about in pt_s 5 to pt_s 2.

All methods employed depend on the use of a compensating beam, in addition to the analyzing beam, to cancel out changes in intensity of light source, scattering effects, and variations in detector efficiency arising from variations in sensitivity of the photomultiplier tubes and oscillograph amplifier circuits used. The analytical and compensating beams can be presented to the experimental system in a cuvette by a variety of mechanical means—vibrating mirrors, rotating sectors, etc.—after which they irradiate a single detector phototube. The output from this tube is passed through an a.c. amplifier and can be monitored to respond only to the a.c. signal so generated, which is proportional to the original absorbancy change. Various means for calibration can be employed. An obvious one is to measure deflections at the oscillograph brought about by known changes in absorbancy.

The two beams can be obtained either by splitting the beam leaving the monochromator ("split beam"), or by using two monochromators ("double beam"). Some details of these methods which apply in particular researches will be presented in the following sections.

Two major approaches are in use. One depends on the use of flash (impulse) spectrophotometry, i.e., a variation of "relaxation" methodology (p. 149), in which transient effects of an initial short pulse of light are detected (see next section). The other involves observation of absorbancy changes which occur in shifts from one steady state to another as a result of constant actinic illumination (see p. 165 *et seq.*). A feature of many researches is the use of a reference wavelength at which the absorbancy change is the same for the two states involved—the so-called "isosbestic" point, after the Greek roots "iso" (same) and "sbestos" (quench, extinguish).

A. Results with Flash Spectrophotometry

Beginning in 1954, H. T. Witt and his collaborators have published observations obtained in an extensive series of researches (36, 37, 38). Their methodology (39) is illustrated in Fig. 22, which displays a block diagram of the apparatus. The photochemical system is contained in a cuvette. Excitation for various periods (from 10^{-5} sec to several min) is afforded by light impulses which pass from the continuous source (S) or from the flash source (F) over the optical paths, (D) or (B). The flashes are generated by discharge of a condenser bank 0.5–200 μF, ca. 3000 volts—symbols (V) and (G). Monochromatic analyzing light (M_1) from the monochromator (M) passes through the cuvette and then falls on the photomultiplier (detector SEV 1). A portion of M_1 can be isolated (M_2) by means of a half-silvered mirror (E) and monitored by a second photomultiplier (SEV 2). The two photocurrents so produced can be passed to a differential amplifier (DA) via a compensator and selector array (KS) so that the two signals are equalized. The electronic switch (ES), synchronizer (SYN), and oscillograph permit visualization of the time course of the emitted signals. The changes in absorbancy in M_1 are passed from SEV 1 through an amplifier (A) to the oscillograph circuit. Fluctuations in M_1 and M_2 are minimized by means of the compensator and differential amplifier setup (KS and

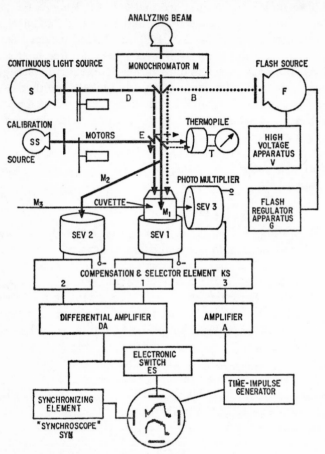

FIG. 22. Block diagram of flash apparatus (see text). After H. T. Witt, R. Moraw, and A. Müller (39).

DA). Thus, small absorbancy changes in the cuvette, of magnitude 0.1% of initial absorbancy, are followed. Calibration is effected by means of a standard source (SS) and a thermopile (T). The variations in duration of the source (S) are obtained by means of rotating sectors driven by motors, as shown. A third detector circuit (SEV 3 to A) is included so that measurements can be made with another analyzing beam (M_3). Thus, it is possible to make readings simultaneously at two selected wavelengths; alternatively, absorption and fluorescence parameters can be studied. The wavelength limits (350–580 mμ) cover the spectral range in which absorption maxima for most biologically important molecules occur.

An extensive list of variables has been studied. These fall into four categories: (*a*) physical change (wavelength, time, temperature from $-200°$ C to $+60°$ C); (*b*) source material (whole cells of plants and bacteria; mutant cells; chromatophores and chloroplasts, untreated or manipulated by heat treatment, extraction with organic solvents, etc.); (*c*) environment (light intensity; pH; pre-exposure; suspension as liquid or in frozen state; anhydrous state or in D_2O); (*d*) chemical inhibition (reversible removal of chlorophyll and Mn^{++}; coupling with oxidation-reduction systems, as in the Hill reaction; coupling with paramagnetic gases). All of these changes are monitored by testing for photochemical function (oxygen evolution) after restoration to normal conditions (40).

Green plant cells exhibit five types of change, called "types 0, 1, 2a, 2b, and 3." Type 0 is a fast process ($\tau_{\frac{1}{2}} \sim 3 \times 10^{-5}$ sec) and is associated with alterations caused by removal of chlorophyll by growth of cells under conditions of nitrate deficiency, by the use of chlorophyll-deficient mutants, or by the use of digitonin. The origin of this type of spectral shift, with characteristic decreases in the Soret region and increases at approximately 530 mμ, can be ascribed to accumulation of triplet-state chlorophyll.

Type 1, found in normal cells, is also a fast process ($\tau_{\frac{1}{2}} \sim 5 \times 10^{-5}$ sec) with a maximum decrease at approximately 435 mμ which corresponds with the absorption maximum of chlorophyll *a in vivo*. A derivative with absorption maximum at 520 mμ is formed. The origin of this spectral type is assumed to be a metastable state different from that responsible for type 0. This deduction rests on the following facts. The change is independent of pH between 3 and 11. It occurs in all species which contain chlorophyll a as the major common photopigment. No alteration is caused by lyophilization or low temperature ($-200°$ C). Reaction time is as fast or faster at $-110°$ C as at room temperature. The change is absent at temperatures higher than $60°$ C. Paramagnetic gases (oxygen, nitric oxide) abolish it. The absorption changes are of such small magnitude as to indicate that only a small fraction of the chlorophyll a present participates in the type 1 reaction.

Type 2 is a slower process ($\tau_{\frac{1}{2}} \sim 10^{-2}$ sec) with a set of absorption changes which show decreases at 420, 475, and 515 mμ. After careful extraction with petroleum ether, the changes at 475 and 515 mμ disappear. These latter changes are classified as type 2b, while that which persists at 420 mμ after extraction is called type 2a. A small change at approximately 530 mμ is seen in type 2a, while type 2b is abolished by the extraction procedure. Type 2b can be restored by addition of the extract to the chloroplasts. Type 2a persists at $-150°$ C, whereas type 2b is lost. The type 2a change at $-150°$ C is not reversed upon switching off the light. The suspension must be thawed to $0°$ C before the back reaction and restoration of the normal dark absorbancy is effected. All of these results are in accord with the early work of L. N. M. Duysens (41) and of B. Chance and L. Smith (42), as well as with the more recent findings of Chance and M. Nishimura (43) for bacteria (to be discussed in the next section), in that they indicate a photochemical oxidation of a heme protein (cytochrome) which has a characteristic Soret absorption maximum in its reduced form at approximately 420–423 mμ.

Type 2b appears very rapidly (ca. 10^{-5} sec) and persists for approximately 10^{-2} sec. The substance formed, labeled "x," has an increased absorption at 515 mμ and a decreased absorption at 475 mμ. Witt *et al.* assume a process symbolized as:

$$x(475\ m\mu) \xrightarrow{\ 10^{-5}\ sec\ } x'(515\ m\mu) \xrightarrow{\ 10^{-2}\ sec\ } x.$$

This reaction is inhibited by lyophilization and low temperature. Incubation with oxidized indophenol, methylene blue, thionine, etc. greatly shortens the reaction x′ →x, an observation which is interpreted to mean that x′ is a reduced form of x. Because petroleum ether extraction abolishes type 2b, the substance involved is assumed to be a quinoidal substance, very probably plastoquinone because of its high concentration in chloroplasts (Chapter II). Estimates of the oxidation potential, obtained from the degree of coupling with the dyes used, indicate $E_m \sim 0$ volts. The slow phase of the type 2b process is considerably affected by manganese deficiency (44), whereas the fast phase, as well as the type 2a change, is not. These facts have been interpreted as support for the notion that Mn^{++} is not involved in the primary process, whereby the photooxidant is generated, but rather in the secondary processes leading to oxygen evolution. This result is of considerable interest because for some years manganese has been considered, on the basis of nutrition studies and investigations on photoreductions, to be essential in the oxygen-evolving system (45).

Type 3 changes are relatively slow ($\tau_{1/2} \sim 10^{-2}$ sec) and are found during the course of the Hill reaction with dichlorophenol-indophenol as Hill oxidant. A decrease in absorption with a band maximum at approximately 600 mμ is observed.

B. Results with Differential Steady-State Spectrophotometry and Spectrofluorimetry

A great body of data has accumulated in the last decade in this area of research, notably from the laboratories of L. N. M. Duysens (41), B. Chance (42, 46), and H. Lundegärdh (47). It is certain that there will be continued activity at a steadily increasing level as the techniques which employ high-sensitivity spectrophotometric and spectrofluorometric methods become more widespread. The split-beam and double-beam methods are now in use in many laboratories for the study of intracellular pigments and components of

respiratory chains (48). When supplemented by flow devices
for control of reaction times, these methods enable kinetic
studies of a variety of important fast reactions, not only in
this era but in the early phases of the enzyme-controlled
systems of the ensuing biochemical era.

The split-beam method, with its high sensitivity and rapid
recording features (49, 50), has been used together with the
double-beam apparatus with particular success to monitor
reactions in the photosynthetic bacteria and chromatophores. Modifications to permit measurements at very low
temperatures (43) (ca. 100° K) enable added discrimination
in analysis of the strictly photochemical components presented in the records obtained from the oscillograph traces.

Space does not permit a complete survey. It will suffice
to describe a single research, that of J. M. Olson and B.
Chance (51), who studied the absorbancy changes and quantum efficiencies of light-induced reactions in whole-cell suspensions of the obligate photoanaerobe *Chromatium*. They
used a double-beam system (see Fig. 23) to record the ab-

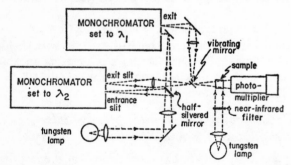

Fig. 23. Double-beam system (see text). After J. M. Olson and B.
Chance (51).

sorbancy changes consequent on irradiation of the bacterial
suspensions by light passed through Wratten No. 88A filters
which transmitted only light with $\lambda > 700$ mμ. (The actinic
region in these bacteria is dominated by the bacteriochlorophyll absorption maximum at 890 mμ, with other maxima

at 800 and 850 mμ.) In this system, the continuous light signal which arose from the scattered actinic beam was rejected, only the modulated and amplified a.c. light signal from the monochromatic analyzing beam being recorded.

The two monochromators transmit light at wavelengths λ_1 and λ_2. The exit beams from the monochromators are directed alternately through the sample by means of the small mirror which is mounted on a 60-cycle vibrating contact of a Brown converter (mechanical switch). Each beam goes through the sample for half a cycle (1/120 sec). The transmitted light then passes to a photomultiplier which generates a signal voltage through a resistor; this voltage is made up of a d.c. component and an a.c. square-wave component. The d.c. component is equal to the average of the two voltage signals which correspond to λ_1 and λ_2, while the a.c. component is equal to the difference between these two voltages. The voltage signals from the resistor are compared to a reference voltage. In the detection circuit the signals from λ_1 and λ_2 are synchronized with the alternation of the two light beams. Only the differences in signal voltages, i.e., the absorbancy changes in the sample, are measured because they are associated with the alternation of the two analyzing beams, whereas the variations in intensity brought about by scattering of the exciting light beam (brought in, as shown, from the side) affect only the d.c. signals which are not registered.

In all exercises of this type, it is essential to begin with a survey of the whole spectrum available, so that, hopefully, one can pick out sets of absorbancy changes which can be correlated with those expected for changes in oxidation levels of known particle components. Hence, the first procedures involved the use of the rapid-recording split-beam apparatus (50) to determine the whole spectrum of absorbancy changes induced in *Chromatium* cells by anaerobic illumination in the infrared. *Chromatium* proved to be the most amenable system of all those tested, because absorbancy changes of this type were not obscured by large shifts in absorption caused by bleaching of chlorophylls and carotenoids, such as complicate measurements in other systems (52).

Having fixed on the heme protein components, Olson and Chance were then in a position, using the double-beam spectrophotometer, to study kinetics of transitions from dark to light states and back, by measurements of absorbancy changes at selected wavelengths [e.g., the Soret maxima (λ 418–425 mμ) for the heme components] as correlated with absorbancy changes at other characteristic maxima in the visible (λ 550–555 mμ and 520–530 mμ). They distinguished a minimum of four such components, as kinetic moieties, which they identified by the placement of the Soret maxima in the difference spectra as C423.5, C426, C422, and C430. The absorbancy changes on illumination all involved decreases in absorbancy, so that the transition from light to dark could be said to involve oxidation of the heme components relative to their initial state in the dark. These photooxidations were found to be insensitive to carbon monoxide and cyanide. Aeration in the dark caused an oxidation of the C426 component (which was also found to be a carbon monoxide-binding pigment) as well as of C423.5. Aeration in the light caused oxidation of C422 and C430, which could be enhanced in all components by addition of the respiratory inhibitor, phenylmercuric acetate. All of these heme moieties could be associated with pure heme proteins isolated previously by R. G. Bartsch and M. D. Kamen (see p. 58).

In later experiments, Chance and M. Nishimura (43) found that a single heme component with a Soret band maximum at approximately 420 mμ was photooxidized at approximately 77° K. The rate constant for oxidation on illumination was altered hardly at all from that found at room temperature. This important result indicated that the oxidation of the heme moiety was independent of temperature and thus could be considered a true photochemical process, as distinct from the other oxidations noted at room temperature. The return to the original state of reduction in the dark was completely inhibited at 77° K.

These and many other observations indicate quite clearly an electron-transfer process involving one of the cytochrome compounds of *Chromatium* and bacteriochlorophyll in the bacterial chromatophore, as a primary reaction in pt_s ~3. Observations with other systems are not as clear-cut because of interference by the reactions involving the photoactive pigments in pt_s ~5 and thereafter (53, 54).

Other components implicated in these studies are typical catalysts present in electron-transfer chains which couple to biosynthesis, e.g., pyridine nucleotides, flavins, quinones. The participation of the bound pyridine nucleotides in chromatophores is best noted by observation of the change in fluorescence which occurs on infrared irradiation of cell suspensions of the photosynthetic bacteria (55–57) and certain algae (58, 59). The demonstration of cellular-reduced bound pyridine nucleotide depends on the fact that only the reduced form fluoresces and that the characteristic excitation wavelength maximum is at 365 mμ, with a characteristic fluorescence maximum at ~440 mμ. In all cases examined, there is invariably an increase in such fluorescence upon irradiation with actinic light. Quantum numbers of ~6 have been quoted (59, 60) for the chloroplast photoreduction of pyridine nucleotide. The kinetics of the process indicate (57) that in chromatophores it lags in time behind the heme protein photooxidation, which in *Chromatium* chromatophores (61) appears to be a process with a quantum number close to one.

In summary, it seems certain that in chromatophores, and very probably in chloroplasts, events in pt_s ~5 involve bleaching of the photoactive pigments, followed by reactions of electron transfer involving the cytochromes and other heme proteins of the photosynthetic apparatus beginning in pt_s ~ 4, as well as later reactions in which pyridine nucleotides are reduced. Shifts in the oxidation states of flavins and quinoidal components undoubtedly occur but their significance and magnitude are uncertain. The status of the photoactivated electron transfer from cytochrome to chlorophyll seems assured in at least one case, that of *Chromatium* chromatophores (43, 51). The mechanism for such a reaction can be visualized in terms of the structures written previously (p. 155) as shown in Fig. 24. Excitation of the

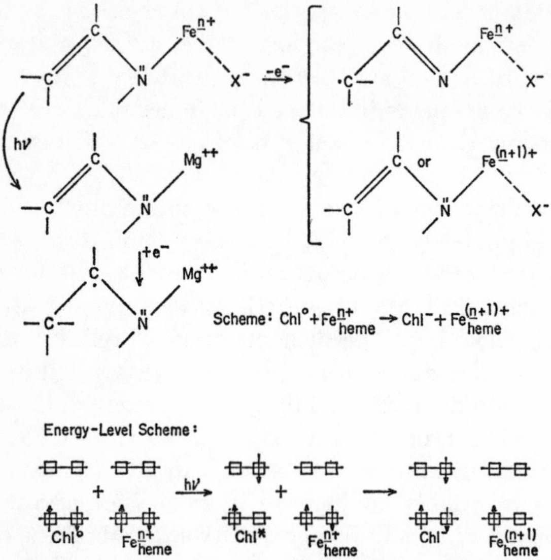

FIG. 24. Structural relations in charge-transfer reaction between chlorophyll and a heme protein. After M. D. Kamen (62,63). Reaction is shown for intermediate singlet state of chlorophyll; "X" is a ligand (see text).

π electron system in the chlorophyll moiety of a chlorophyll-cytochrome adduct would result in an empty ground orbital which could be filled by migration of a π electron from the cytochrome system. The result would be a new compound in which both moieties, the resultant chlorophyll negative ion and the cytochrome-positive ion, would be in new ground states. The further fate of these ions would be determined by the systems coupled to them, as discussed on p. 142 *et seq.* More extensive speculations on this type of mechanism have been presented by M. D. Kamen (62, 63).

An alternative mechanism supposes prior loss of the excited electron from chlorophyll to a hydrogen acceptor, leaving a positive chlorophyll ion which would then accept an electron from the cytochrome. H. T. Witt, A. Müller, and B. Rumberg interpret their most recent findings (63a) as indicating such a process. The data at hand do not permit a decision between these alternatives.

V. The Two-Quantum Process in Chloroplasts

The crucial observations by R. Emerson and his collaborators which have led to the hypothesis that two separate one-quantum processes are needed to initiate oxygen evolution and complete the primary phase of chloroplast photosynthesis have been reviewed in a definitive paper by R. Emerson and E. Rabinowitch (64). Many investigators directly concerned with events between pt_s 9 and pt_s 4 have offered data and have suggested working hypotheses based on the existence of this "second Emerson effect."

The evidence indicates that the two quanta are absorbed by different groups of pigments which cooperate in the primary photochemistry. The nature of these processes is unknown and all that can be offered at present are a few of the various speculations in the literature to date (63–70). Practically all schemes feature involvement of the *c*-type cytochromes in the photosynthetic apparatus as an intermediate or tie point between the two systems postulated, one of which works at the reducing end and the other at the oxidizing end of the potential gap created by any of the various processes discussed in Chapter III.

H. T. Witt, A. Müller, and B. Rumberg (69) have applied their impulse spectrophotometry procedures (see previous section) in an attempt to determine which of the *in vivo* forms of chlorophyll *a* produces their type 2a product. They find that exposure at approximately 670 mμ excites both pigments (Chl *a*670 and Chl *a*680) to give types 2a and 2b absorbancy changes. Exposure at approximately 710 mμ excites mainly Chl *a*680 and results in a marked reduction of the change ascribed to type 2b, while it leaves the type

2a change essentially unaffected. Because the absorbancy changes of type 2a have been assigned to oxidation of a heme protein (probably cytochrome *f*), they reason that Chl *a*680 mediates photooxidation of an oxidant at a potential near zero volt.

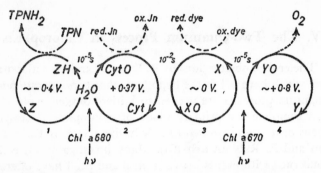

FIG. 25. Reaction scheme of photosynthesis. "Jn" stands for 2,6 dichlorphenolindophenol, other symbols as in text. After H. T. Witt, A. Müller, and B. Rumberg (69).

The reaction pattern they postulate is shown in Fig. 25. ZH is a reductant, YO an oxidant; each is generated by a separate reaction triggered by each of the two pigment systems, as shown.

L. N. M. Duysens, J. Amesz, and B. M. Kamp (66) have investigated the action spectrum for photooxidation of the *c*-type cytochrome in the alga, *Porphyridium cruentum*. A maximum occurs at 680 mμ, with a much lower maximum at 560 mμ ascribed to absorption by phycoerythrin. This result is diametrically opposed to the older findings (p. 116) which showed that 680 mμ excitation of photosynthesis and chlorophyll fluorescence is less efficient than that due to 560 mμ excitation. Duysens *et al.* conclude from this observation that two systems which they call "1" and "2" are involved, and present a scheme as shown in Fig. 26.

B. Kok and G. Hoch (54), from observations on the bleaching of their "P-700" pigment (see p. 44), assume that one of the quantum processes is associated with the bulk of chlorophyll *a*, while the other is activated by an accessory

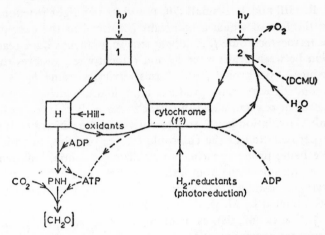

FIG. 26. Reaction scheme of L. N. M. Duysens, J. Amesz, and B. M. Kamp (66) (see text). PnH = Pyridine nucleotide system.

pigment which is coupled to a small fraction of the chlorophyll *a*. The two systems converge on "P-700" which is both oxidized and reduced. The scheme is visualized in Fig. 27.

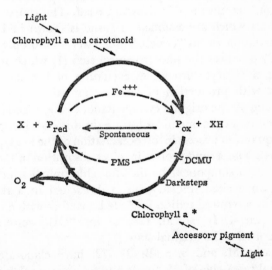

FIG. 27. Reaction diagram for two-step photosynthesis (see text). After B. Kok and G. Hoch (54).

R. Hill and F. Bendall (70) postulate two light reactions, in the first of which a reductant is formed at the expense of ferrocytochrome f. A subsequent spontaneous dark reaction between cytochrome b_6 and cytochrome f restores the reduced cytochrome f and forms ferricytochrome b_6. The second light reaction produces an oxidant, which is a precursor of oxygen, while the cytochrome b_6 is reduced to its initial oxidation level. An alternative scheme which involves hyperoxidation of the chloroplast heme proteins, in which the heme protein reaches an oxidizing potential sufficient to extract electrons from water (e.g., Fe^{4+} and Fe^{5+} valence states, as assumed to exist in peroxidases and catalases) has been offered by M. D. Kamen (62, 63).

J. Franck (67, 68), as mentioned previously (p. 141), has presented some suggestions based on the notion that a single chlorophyll molecule can collect the energy of two quanta. His scheme involves formation of an enol complex between chlorophyll and a photooxidant produced in the initial light reaction. Thus, attention is fixed on the isopentanone structure as the focus of the photosensitization processes, rather than on the macrocyclic structure itself. The course of the reactions which are assumed to ensue is shown in Fig. 28.

Irradiation of an "exposed" (or "wet") chlorophyll (see p. 133) produces the photochemical step (1) which involves chemical change through de-excitation of the metastable Chl a with production of an unsaturated alcohol (enol) grouping on the original cyclopentanone ring, together with enolization of the organic substrate (in this case, lactic acid). This quantum process involves excitation of the n-π type (pp. 96, 134). The second process involves absorption of the short wavelength component by the enol chlorophyll which produces an excited singlet. This is de-excited in a reaction whereby a reduced radical is created, together with a chlorophyll (Enz–OH) radical. Loss of the "OH" restores the chlorophyll to its original state (71).

Finally, M. and S. S. Brody (72) have elaborated the original researches of M. Brody and R. Emerson (73) on the Emerson effect in *Porphyridium cruentum* by a study of changes in relative efficiencies of the phycoerythrin-sensitized photosynthesis induced by variations in wavelengths of light used for culture of the algae. They have examined the quantum yields (q_F) at various wavelengths as a function of the ratio of the accessory pigment to the chlorophyll present, under various conditions of illumination. They find that

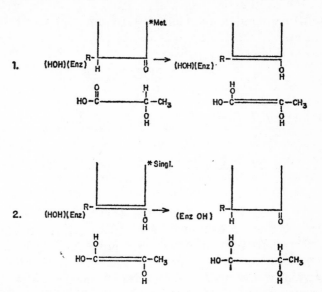

Fig. 28. Reaction mechanism for storage of two quanta (see text). After J. Franck (67,68).

exposure to green light (phycoerythrin absorption) evokes maximal values for q_F in the green, while exposure to blue light (chlorophyll absorption) depresses the values of q_F in the green. These results indicate some of the complexities which can be expected with further research on the Emerson effect. The Brodys present an interpretation based on the notion that two types of chlorophyll exist, between which energy transfer efficiency can be varied as a result of adaptation to different culture conditions.

It is evident that events in the chromatophore in this era are distinguished from those in the chloroplast by the in-

clusion in the latter of an accessory system for production of
oxidation potentials sufficient to effect a liberation of
oxygen, simultaneous with the production of reductants at
a potential sufficient to reduce carbon dioxide to the oxidation level of carbohydrate. In terms of the diagram (Fig.
2 in Chapter I) given previously, the chromatophore process
involves creation of a potential gap only about half as great
as that produced in the chloroplast. In terms of the schemes
presented in this section, only one of the two reaction systems of chloroplasts is present in chromatophores, e.g., "system 1" in Fig. 26. The chromatophore scheme presented at
the end of Chapter III is an elaboration of suggestions
offered on the nature of the cytochrome-mediated processes
in the various schemes of Figs. 25, 26, and 27.

VI. Prospects for the Biochemical Era;
pt_s 4 and Beyond

The reader will recall that the definition proposed for
events in the era defined by the limits pt_s 9 to pt_s 4 (p.
5) characterizes photosynthesis as a process in which electronic excitation of chlorophyll is quenched during chemical
reactions which produce high-energy systems possessing excess amounts, as well as deficiencies, of electrons. The jour-
ney from pt_s 15 to pt_s 4 is now complete, and the reader may
inquire whether more than this can be said. Certainly no
definite extension in terms of specific chemical systems can
be presented. For the biochemist, who enters the study
of photosynthesis as the events described in this book come
to an end, there is only the surmise that, by pt_s 4, the ex-
cesses and deficiencies of electrons (and protons) have been
stabilized by a spatial separation into equivalent amounts
of reducing and oxidizing systems. The components of the
former may be semireduced forms of the photoactive pigments, pyridine nucleotides, and possibly those compounds
typical of the reducing end of respiratory chains, such as
flavins, sulfhydryl compounds, and quinones. As for the oxi-

dizing systems, there is more than a suggestion that, in chromatophores, oxidized heme proteins constitute the major portion of such systems, and that in chloroplasts they also play a role in the oxidizing mechanisms.

If a chain of oxidation catalysts is assumed to exist in the photosynthetic apparatus, analogous to that in mitochondria with the added feature that a typical oxidase is absent, then the biochemical era can be imagined to open with electron (and proton)-transfer processes in which the potential gap created between pt_s 15 and pt_s 4 is closed by backflow of electrons; the energy so released is coupled to synthetic processes, such as ATP formation and carbon dioxide assimilation. It remains for future research to fill in the details of mechanisms and chemical nature of intermediates which bridge the gap between pt_s 4 and the final synthesis of cellular material.

References*

1. M. Eigen and L. DeMaeyer, *Z. Elektrochem.* **59,** 986 (1955).
2. M. Eigen and J. Schoen, *Z. Elektrochem.* **59,** 483 (1955).
3. For a review, see M. Eigen, *in* "Techniques of Organic Chemistry" (S. L. Friess, E. S. Lewis, and A. Weissberger, eds.), Vol. VIII, Part 2, Chapters 14–20. Interscience, New York, 1962.
4. For a review, see A. Weller, *Prog. Reaction Kinetics* **1,** 189 (1961).
5. A. Weller, *Z. phys. Chem. (Frankfurt)* [N.F.] **17,** 224 (1958).
6. T. Förster, *Z. Elektrochem.* **54,** 42 (1951).
7. A. Terenin and A. Kiriakin, *Nature* **139,** 881 (1947).
8. T. Förster and K. Kasper, *Z. phys. Chem. (Frankfurt)* [N.F.] **1,** 19 (1954).
9. S. Ainsworth, *J. Phys. Chem.* **64,** 715 (1960).
10. H. Linschitz and L. Pekkarinen, *J. Am. Chem. Soc.* **82,** 2411 (1960).
11. R. S. Livingston, see Gen. ref. II, p. 830 et seq., and symposium ref. [6], p. 196 et seq.
12. A. A. Krasnovsky, *Ann. Rev. Plant Physiol.* **12,** 155 (1961).
13. E. Rabinowitch and J. Weiss, *Proc. Roy. Soc.* **A162,** 2511 (1937).
14. G. Weber and F. W. J. Teale, *Trans. Faraday Soc.* **54,** 640 (1958).
15. S. S. Brody and M. Brody, *Trans. Faraday Soc.* **58,** 416 (1962).

* Complete information pertaining to symposium references [1] to [7] and general references I, II, and III can be found in Section VI (Collateral Reading) of Chapter I.

16. A. S. Holt, *Proc. 5th Intern. Congr. Biochem., Moscow, 1961,* in press, Pergamon Press, New York; see also *Can. J. Biochem. and Physiol.* **36,** 439 (1958).

17. N. K. King and M. E. Winfield, *Australian J. Chem.* **12,** 47 (1959); see also M. E. Winfield, *in* "Haematin Enzymes," Symposium No. 19, IUB, Canberra (J. E. Falk, R. Lemberg, and R. K. Morton, eds.), Part 1, p. 245 et seq. Pergamon Press, New York (1961), for a discussion of electronic structures which involve abnormal iron valences, as in catalase and peroxidase.

18. J. C. Goedheer, symposium ref. [4], p. 325.

18a. S. Gillman and H. Linschitz, in preparation (1962); see also S. Gilman, Doctoral Thesis, Syracuse University, Syracuse, New York (1960).

19. A. A. Krasnovsky, *Doklady Akad. Nauk S.S.S.R.* **60,** 421 (1948).

20. V. B. Evstigneev and V. A. Gavrilova, *Doklady Akad. Nauk S.S.S.R.* **95,** 841 (1954).

21. A. A. Krasnovsky and G. P. Brin, *Doklady Akad. Nauk S.S.S.R.* **96,** 1025 (1954).

22. V. V. Evstigneev and V. A. Gavrilova, *Doklady Akad. Nauk S.S.S.R.* **96,** 1017 (1954).

22a. V. V. Evstigneev and V. A. Gavrilova, *Doklady Akad. Nauk S.S.S.R.* **91,** 899 (1953).

23. B. Rackow and H. Konig, *Z. Elektrochem.* **62,** 482 (1958).

24. H. Linschitz and S. Weissman, *Arch. Biochem. Biophys.* **67,** 491 (1957).

24a. S. S. Brody, G. Newell and T. Castner, *J. Phys. Chem.* **64,** 554 (1960).

25. S. S. Brody, *J. Am. Chem. Soc.* **82,** 1570 (1960).

26. G. Zieger and H. T. Witt, *Z. Physik. Chem. (Frankfurt)* [N.F.] **28,** 286 (1961).

27. R. S. Livingston and R. Pariser, *J. Am. Chem. Soc.* **78,** 2948 (1956).

28. R. S. Livingston and R. Pariser, *J. Am. Chem. Soc.* **70,** 1510 (1948).

29. A. A. Burentch, *Doklady Akad. Nauk S.S.S.R.* **91,** 1221 (1953).

30. A. A. Krasnovsky and K. K. Voinovskaya, *Doklady Akad. Nauk S.S.S.R.* **87,** 109 (1952).

31. A. A. Krasnovsky, *Doklady Akad. Nauk S.S.S.R.* **61,** 91 (1948).

32. A. A. Krasnovsky and G. P. Brin, *Doklady Akad. Nauk S.S.S.R.* **67,** 325 (1949).

33. E. Fujimori, quoted in (11), p. 869.

34. A. A. Krasnovsky, *Doklady Akad. Nauk S.S.S.R.* **103,** 283 (1955).

35. A. A. Krasnovsky and K. K. Voinovskaya, *Biophys. Akad. Nauk (URSS),* **1,** 120 (1956).

35a. L. P. Vernon, *Acta Chem. Scand.* **15,** 1630, 1651 (1961).

35b. G. Zieger and H. T. Witt, *Z. physik. Chem. (Frankfurt)* [N.F.] **28,** 286 (1961).

36. H. T. Witt, *Naturwissenschaften* **42**, 72 (1955).
37. H. T. Witt, *Z. Physik. Chem.* [N.F.] **4**, 120 (1955).
38. H. T. Witt, *Z. Elektrochem.* **59**, 891 (1955).
39. Details of the experimental setup can be found in the article by H. T. Witt, R. Moraw, and A. Müller, *Z. Physik. Chem. (Frankfurt)* [N.F.] **20**, 13 (1959).
40. A list of articles from the Witt group follows (all references in *Z. Physik. Chem. (Frankfurt)* [N.F.]: **12**, 393; **13**, 8; **13**, 119; **20**, 17; **20**, 283; **21**, 1; **23**, 133; **28**, 18; **29**, 1; **29**, 13; **29**, 25. Most recently, new results which require changes in interpretation of previous data have appeared in *Nature*, **194**, 854 (1962).
41. L. N. M. Duysens, *Science* **120**, 353 (1954).
42. B. Chance and L. Smith, *Nature* **175**, 803 (1955).
43. B. Chance and M. Nishimura, *Proc. Natl. Acad. Sci. U.S.* **46**, 12 (1960).
44. E. Kessler, R. Moraw, B. Rumberg, and H. T. Witt, Gen. ref. II, Vol. 1, p. 634 et seq.; *Biochim. et Biophys. Acta* **43**, 193 (1960).
45. E. Kessler, *Planta* **49**, 435 (1957).
46. B. Chance, *Nature* **169**, 215 (1952).
47. H. Lundegärdh, *Arkiv. Kemi.* **3**, 69 (1951).
48. B. Chance, in "Methods in Enzymology" (N. O. Kaplan and S. Colowick, eds.), Vol. IV, p. 273 et seq. Academic Press, New York, 1957.
49. B. Chance, *Science* **120**, 707 (1959).
50. C. C. Yang and V. Legallais, *Rev. Sci. Inst.* **25**, 801 (1954).
51. J. M. Olson and B. Chance, *Arch. Biochem. Biophys.* **88**, 26, 40 (1960).
52. L. Smith and J. Ramirez, *J. Biol. Chem.* **235**, 219 (1960).
53. B. Chance and M. Nishimura, *Proc. 5th Intern. Cong. Biochem., Moscow, 1961* Symposium VI, in press.
54. See G. Hoch and B. Kok, *Ann. Rev. Plant Physiol.* **12**, 155 (1961) for a review of work on chloroplast processes.
55. J. M. Olson and J. Amesz, *Biochim. et Biophys. Acta* **37**, 14 (1960).
56. J. M. Olson, L. M. N. Duysens, and G. H. M. Kronenberg, *Biochim. et Biophys. Acta* **36**, 125 (1959).
57. J. M. Olson and B. Chance, *Arch. Biochem. Biophys.* **88**, 20 (1960).
58. L. N. M. Duysens and G. Sweep, *Biochim. et Biophys. Acta,* **25**, 13 (1957).
59. J. Amesz and L. N. M. Nuysens, *Faraday Soc. Discussions No.* **27**, 173 (1959).
60. L. N. M. Duysens and J. Amesz, *Plant Physiol.* **34**, 210 (1959). These authors present more recent data in *Biochim. et Biophys. Acta* **64**, 243, 261 (1962).
61. J. M. Olson, *Science* **135**, 101 (1962).
62. M. D. Kamen, *in* "Biological Structure and Function," First

IUB/IUBS Intern. Symposium, Stockholm, 1960 (T. W. Goodwin and O. Lindberg, eds.), Vol. 2, p. 277 et seq. Academic Press, New York, 1961.

63. M. D. Kamen, symposium ref. [7], p. 483 et seq.
63a. H. T. Witt, A. Müller, and B. Rumberg, *Nature* 192, 967 (1961).
64. R. Emerson and E. Rabinowitch, *Plant Physiol.* 35, 477 (1960).
65. C. S. French, symposium ref. [7], p. 447 et seq.
66. L. N. M. Duysens, J. Amesz, and B. M. Kamp, *Nature* 190, 510 (1961).
67. J. Franck, *Proc. Natl. Acad. Sci. U.S.* 44, 941 (1958).
68. J. Franck, *Arch. Biochem. Biophys.* 80, 378 (1959).
69. H. T. Witt, A. Müller, and B. Rumberg, *Nature* 191, 194 (1961).
70. R. Hill and F. Bendall, *Nature* 186, 136 (1960).
71. For an extended discussion, see J. Franck, J. L. Rosenberg, and C. Weiss, ref. (32) Chapter III.
72. M. Brody and S. S. Brody, *Arch. Biochem. Biophys.* 92, 354 (1962).
73. M. Brody and R. Emerson, *J. Gen. Physiol.* 43, 251 (1959).

Subject Index

A

Aspidistra sp., 69
Athiorhodaceae, 19

B

Bacterial photosynthesis, 16
Bacteriochlorophyll, 7
  excitation of, 136, 137, 142
  spectroscopy of, 61–62, 166–167
  structure of, 54
Bacterioviridin, 7
Biochemical era, 5

C

Carbon dioxide, assimilation, 8
Carotenes and carotenoids energy transfer, 116–117
  structures, 27–30
Catalase, 35, 59
Chemiluminescence, 134–135
Chloraceae, 18
Chlorobium thiosulfatophilum, 54
Chlorophyll, 7, 8
  dimeric, 120–123
  fluorescence polarization, 101–105
  molecular spectroscopy, 94–135
  photochemistry, 154–159
  triplet state, 123–130
  "wet" and "dry," 133–134
Chlorophyll *a*, 25, 44, 91–92
  absorption spectra, 38–41, 94–99, 126–127, 133
  dichroism and birefringence, 99–101
  energy transfer, 116–120
  fluorescence decay, 91–92
  in vitro fluorescence, 107–116
  in vivo absorption, 163–164, 171–172

in vivo fluorescence, 108–113, 116, 121, 133–134
Chlorophyll *b*, 25, 38, 107
Chlorophyll *c*, 25, 34, 52
Chlorophyll *d*, 25
Chlorophyllides, 27
Chloroplast, 22
  composition, 24–44
  dichroism, 66–70,
  energy transfer, 118–119
  fine structure, 66–70
  nonphotochemical components, 30–36
  photoactive pigments, 25–30
  polarized fluorescence, 69–70
  quantum numbers and action spectra, 37–44
  structure and development, 45–49
  two-quantum process, 171–176
Chromatium, 69–70
  chromatophores, 50–53, 58–59
Chromatophore, 22, 136
  action spectra, 60–63
  components, 54–60
  composition, 49–54
  development, 63–65
  energy transfer, 117, 118–119
  photosynthesis, 142–143
  spectrophotometry, 169–170
  two-quantum process, 174–176
Closterium chloroplasts, 68–69
Coenzyme Q, occurrence, 55–57
  structure, 32–33
Copper, 33
Cytochromes, 59
  energy transfer, 142, 169
Cytochrome *c*, photooxidation, 159
Cytochrome *f*, occurrence, 34–35